Managing Reality

Book Two
Procuring an Engineering and Construction Contract

Third edition

Other titles in the Managing Reality series:

Managing Reality. Book One: Introduction to the Engineering and Construction Contract. Third edition (2017)
Bronwyn Mitchell and Barry Trebes. ISBN 978-0-7277-6182-8

Managing Reality. Book Three: Managing the Contract. Third edition (2017)
B. Mitchell and B. Trebes. ISBN 978-0-7277-6186-6

Managing Reality. Book Four: Managing Change. Third edition (2017)
B. Mitchell and B. Trebes. ISBN 978-0-7277-6188-0

Managing Reality. Book Five: Managing Procedures. Third edition (2017)
B. Mitchell and B. Trebes. ISBN 978-0-7277-6190-3

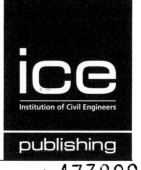

Managing Reality

Book Two
Procuring an Engineering and Construction Contract

Third edition

Bronwyn Mitchell and Barry Trebes

Published by ICE Publishing, One Great George Street, Westminster, London SW1P 3AA.

Full detail of ICE Publishing representatives and distributors can be found at:
www.icebookshop.com/bookshop_contact.asp

Other titles by ICE Publishing:
NEC4: The Role of the Project Manager
B. Mitchell and B. Trebes. ISBN 978-0-7277-6353-2
NEC4: The Role of the Supervisor
B. Mitchell and B. Trebes. ISBN 978-0-7277-6355-6
NEC3 and NEC4 Compared
R. Gerrard. ISBN 978-0-7277-6201-6

www.icebookshop.com

A catalogue record for this book is available from the British Library

ISBN 978-0-7277-6184-2

© Thomas Telford Limited 2018

ICE Publishing is a division of Thomas Telford Ltd, a wholly-owned subsidiary of the Institution of Civil Engineers (ICE).

Commissioning Editor: Michael Fenton
Production Editor: Madhubanti Bhattacharyya
Market Development Executive: Elizabeth Hobson

FSC
www.fsc.org
MIX
Paper from
responsible sources
FSC® C019520

Typeset by Academic + Technical, Bristol
Index created by Laurence Errington
Printed and bound by NOVOPRINT S.A., Spain

Contents

Preface

In the preface to the first edition of *Managing Reality*, in 2005, we set out our aims and aspirations for 'managing reality'. These were as follows:

- to add and contribute to the body of knowledge on the use of the NEC Engineering and Construction Contract (ECC)
- to provide a set of books that focuses on the 'how to' – how to manage and administer the ECC contract
- to present as a five-part book series that covers both the needs of the student professional or prospective client, through to the novice practitioner and experienced user
- to provide a rounded view of the ECC, whatever your discipline, on both sides of the contractual relationship
- to enable everyone to realise the business benefits from using the NEC suite of contracts generally and the ECC in particular.

Managing Reality does not attempt to give a legal treatise or a blow-by-blow review of each and every clause. It is intended to be complementary to other publications, which give excellent theoretical and legal perspectives.

This book is about dealing with the reality of real life projects: managing reality.

The feedback and support we have received since the first publication of *Managing Reality* in 2005 has been universally positive, and we would like to thank all of you who have bought and used it since its first publication.

We have greatly enjoyed updating and working on this third edition, and we hope that these books continue to provide a useful body of knowledge on the use of the NEC4 ECC.

Bronwyn Mitchell and Barry Trebes
2017

Foreword

A key objective of the first edition of *Managing Reality* was to provide a five-part book series to meet the needs of students, prospective clients, novice practitioners and experienced users. Satisfying such diverse needs is an ambitious objective for any text.

Does *Managing Reality* achieve its stated aim? I believe that the answer to this is a resounding 'yes'. In my view, the calibre of authorship is exceptional. All levels of and types of readership from the uninitiated to the experienced professional will derive considerable benefit from this text. Although written in a very accessible style, there is no skimping on detail or on addressing difficult issues. The worked examples are particularly helpful. *Managing Reality* should be your prime aid from the moment you are considering whether or not to use an NEC contract right through to using and operating the contract.

But *Managing Reality* is much more than simply a 'how to' guide. It seeks to deliver a clear message that NEC contracts cannot be used to their full potential unless one is prepared to ditch one's knowledge and experience of traditional contracting. For example, emphasis is placed on the fact that certainty and predictability are the hallmarks of NEC contracts. Open-ended and subjective phrases and concepts have no place in NEC contracting.

I am privileged to be associated with this third edition of *Managing Reality*. Its publication is very timely since it coincides with the publication of the NEC4 suite of contracts. This new edition of the NEC suite is a reflection of the dominant position that NEC contracts now have both in the UK and in many other countries. It will continue to support those who need help overcoming any reservations about using NEC contracts, and reinforce existing users in their continued use of these ground-breaking contracts.

Professor Rudi Klein
President, NEC Users' Group

Acknowledgements

We would like to thank the following individuals and companies who have supported this book.

For their active participation in this book we would like to thank

- Professor Rudi Klein (SEC Group Chief Executive) for writing the Foreword
- Dr Robert N. Hunter of Hunter and Edgar Edinburgh for his thoughts and suggested revisions for this third edition
- Michael Fenton, the ICE commissioning editor, for his enthusiasm and patience
- Richard Patterson of Mott MacDonald
- everyone who has given feedback on this book since 2005.

And our continued gratitude to those who provided support and input into the first edition of *Managing Reality*:

- Mike Attridge, of Ellenbrook Consulting, who reviewed this book on behalf of the authors
- David H. Williams, who provided guidance and support in the development of the first edition of this book
- everyone at Needlemans Limited Construction Consultants (now part of the Mott MacDonald Group)
- everyone at MPS Limited with whom Needlemans Limited worked to develop the first web-based management system for the NEC in 2000.

Finally, we would like to thank our family and friends for their ongoing support, understanding and patience.

Series contents

The following outlines the content of the five books in the series.

- emphasises the importance of early dispute resolution to the successful outcome of a contract
- considers the common sources of dispute
- considers how the ECC has been designed to reduce the incidence of disputes
- examines how the ECC provides for the resolution of disputes
- looks at the implications for the dispute resolution process as a result of the HGCR Act as amended
- looks at ECC changes in relation to adjudication.

Book 4   Managing Reality: Managing Change

Chapter 1   **Compensation events**
This chapter describes

- the compensation events contained within the ECC
- procedure for administering compensation events
- roles played by the two main parties to the contract in relation to compensation events.

Appendix 1   **Compensation event procedure**

Chapter 2   **Schedule of Cost Components and Short Schedule of Cost Components**
This chapter discusses aspects relating to the full SCC and its short version, the SSCC, including

- when the SCC and SSCC are used
- how the SCC and SSCC interact with the payment clauses
- Defined Cost
- the Fee
- the components of cost included under the SCC and SSCC
- Contract Data part two.

Appendix 2   **Example quotations for compensation events**

Appendix 3   **Example people cost calculations**

Appendix 4   **Comparison between traditional preliminaries build-up and how they relate to the Schedule of Cost Components and the Short Schedule of Cost Components**

Appendix 5   **Interrelationship between the *Contractor's* and the Subcontractor's *share* on target cost contracts**

Book 5   Managing Reality: Managing Procedures

Chapter 1   **ECC Management: Procedures**
This chapter brings together all the aspects discussed in previous chapters in Books One to Four of the *Managing Reality* series. This chapter provides the 'how to' part of the series. It introduces some example pro formas for use with the ECC. Unless detailed separately due to a complex procedure, replies are described under the relevant action.

For quick reference, this chapter may be read on its own. It does not, however, detail the reasons for carrying out the actions, or the clause numbers that should be referred to in order to verify the actions in accordance with the contract. These are described in detail in the other book's that form part of this series.

Procuring an Engineering and Construction Contract
ISBN 978-0-7277-6184-2

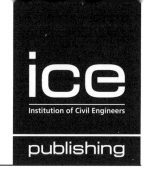

Introduction

General

This series of books will provide the people who are actually using the Engineering and Construction Contract (ECC) in particular, and the New Engineering Contract (NEC) suite in general, practical guidance as to how to prepare and manage an ECC contract with confidence and knowledge of the effects of their actions on the contract and the Parties.

Each book in the series addresses a different area of the management of an ECC contract:

- Book One – *Managing Reality: Introduction to the Engineering and Construction Contract*
- Book Two – *Managing Reality: Procuring an Engineering and Construction Contract*
- Book Three – *Managing Reality: Managing the Contract*
- Book Four – *Managing Reality: Managing Change*
- Book Five – *Managing Reality: Managing Procedures*.

Book One (*Managing Reality: Introduction to the Engineering and Construction Contract*) is for those who are considering using the ECC but need further information, or those who are already using the ECC but need further insight into its rationale. It therefore focuses on the fundamental cultural changes and mind-shift that are required to successfully manage the practicalities of the ECC in use.

Book Two (*Managing Reality: Procuring an Engineering and Construction Contract*) is for those who need to know how to procure an ECC contract. It covers in practical detail the invitations to tender, evaluation of submissions, which option to select, how to complete the Contract Data and how to prepare the Scope. The use of this guidance is appropriate for clients, contractors (including subcontractors) and construction professionals generally.

Book Three (*Managing Reality: Managing the Contract*) is essentially for those who use the contract on a daily basis, covering the detail of practical management such as paying the contractor, reviewing the programme, ensuring the quality of the *works*, and dispute resolution. Both first-time and experienced practitioners will benefit from this book.

Book Four (*Managing Reality: Managing Change*) is for those who are managing change under the contract; whether for the client or the contractor (or subcontractor), the management of change is often a major challenge whatever the form of contract. The ECC deals with change in a different way to other, more traditional forms. This book sets out the steps to efficiently and effectively manage change, bridging the gap between theory and practice.

Book Five (*Managing Reality: Managing Procedures*) gives step-by-step guidance on how to apply the most commonly-used procedures, detailing the actions needed by all Parties to comply with the contract. Anyone administering the contract will benefit from this book.

Background

The ECC could be termed a 'modern contract' in that it seeks to holistically align the setting up of a contract to match business needs, as opposed to writing a contract that merely administers construction events.

The whole ethos of the ECC, and the NEC suite generally, is one of simplicity of language and clarity of requirement. It is important that the roles and responsibilities of all those involved in the contract are equally clear in definition and ownership.

When looking at the ECC for the first time it is easy to believe that it is relatively straightforward and simple. However, this apparent simplicity belies the need for the people involved to think about their project and their role, and how the ECC can deliver their particular contract strategy.

The ECC provides a structured flexible framework for setting up an appropriate form of contract whatever the selected procurement route. The fundamental requirements are as follows:

- The Scope – quality and completeness: what are you asking the *Contractor* to do?
- The Site Information: what are the site conditions that the *Contractor* will find?
- The Contract Data – key objectives for completion (e.g. start date, completion date and programme): when do you want it completed?

The details contained in this series of books will underline the relevance and importance of the above three fundamental requirements.

The structure of the books

Each chapter starts with a synopsis of what is included in that chapter. Throughout the book there are shaded 'practical tip' boxes that immediately point the user towards important reminders for using the ECC (see example below).

> Clarity and completeness of the Scope is fundamental.

There are also unshaded boxes that contain examples to illustrate the text (see example below).

> Imagine a situation in which the *Supervisor* notifies the *Contractor* that the reinstatement of carriageways on a utility diversion project is not to the highway authority's usual standards. However, the Scope is silent about the reinstatement.
>
> The test of a Defect is also whether the work is in accordance with the applicable law. In this instance, the reinstatement is not in accordance with the Road and Street Works Act 1991.

Other diagrams and tables are designed to maintain interest and provide another medium of explanation. There are also standard forms for use in the administration and management of the contract, together with examples.

Throughout the books, the following terms have been used in a specific way:

- NEC is the abbreviation for the suite of New Engineering Contracts and it is not the name of any single contract
- ECC is the abbreviation for the contract in the NEC suite called the Engineering and Construction Contract.

The NEC4 suite comprises the

- Engineering and Construction Contract
- Engineering and Construction Subcontract
- Engineering and Construction Short Contract
- Engineering and Construction Short Subcontract
- Professional Service Contract
- Professional Service Short Contract
- Term Service Contract
- Term Service Short Contract
- Supply Contract
- Supply Short Contract
- Framework Contract
- Dispute Resolution Service Contract
- Design Build and Operate Contract
- Alliance Contract – consultative version.

Procuring an Engineering and Construction Contract
ISBN 978-0-7277-6184-2

Chapter 1
Procurement

Synopsis

This chapter looks at the concept of procurement and contracting strategies and discusses

- procurement and contract strategy
- what tender documents to include in an ECC invitation to tender
- how to draft and compile a contract using the ECC
- procurement scenarios that a client could face and how to approach them
- what are framework agreements and how they could incorporate the ECC
- what is partnering and how it can be used with the ECC.

1.1. What is procurement?

Procurement can be defined as obtaining by purchase, lease or other legal means, plant, equipment, materials, services and works required by an organisation.

The process of procurement commences when a need has been established and ends when the project has been delivered. The accurate definition of the business need is essential prior to attempting to undertake any form of procurement process, and the need must reflect the full-life value of the project; that is, what the project must deliver over a defined period. It should be recognised that in many instances the project goes beyond the physical works and also extends into the operational phase of a project.

Procurement can be a lengthy and complex process, and the potential for waste and error is high. The procurement process usually involves a range of different stakeholders, and people's expectations of the process need to be carefully managed in terms of timescale issues and the fact that stakeholder needs will vary, as well as the usual needs/wants dilemma. The more effort and thought that are invested in the procurement process, the lower the potential for disputes during the contract period.

While it is often tempting to try to procure a solution quickly, it is important that sufficient time is allowed for effective procurement to take place. It is important that all factors should be considered, encompassing the technical, legal and commercial aspects of the project and the accompanying risks. Narrowing procurement criteria to consider price and the end-product may only distort, or ultimately prevent, the achievement of the original objectives of the procurement exercise.

It is advisable or even essential that, wherever possible, all necessary commercial and contractual discussions have been executed prior to work commencing. Failure to do so will mean that both parties are working at risk and could result in disagreements, which are difficult to resolve, as the intended and actual basis of the proposed contract may be open to different interpretations by each party (or the basis of the original agreement could even be forgotten).

> Procurement involves not only commercial and contractual matters but also technical, health and safety, environmental, sustainability, security and all other aspects of the project.

When considering the procurement of a solution to meet a business need, clients should use all of their knowledge on not only the technical aspects of the product or works but also on the commercial aspects. The following is a list of the types of items that should be considered when planning a procurement exercise:

- operational requirements/end-user consultation
- the client's requirements/specification, whether functional, performance or technical (quality, fitness for purpose, minimum performance standards)
- the time-frame (programme)
- the lifetime or 'whole-life' cost of the project (life-cycle costing/costs in use), including maintenance and operation
- possible tender list
- pricing factors, including a pricing programme, cash flow issues, guarantees and pricing risk
- the required level of insurance cover
- environmental, economic and social sustainability considerations
- health and safety matters
- security
- risk
- project inhibitors (e.g. site constraints, site limitations and availability)
- impact on business (e.g. disruption to business activities during works).

1.2. Value for money

The concept of value for money is not the same as accepting the lowest-priced offer. A value-for-money approach is a move away from the policy of accepting lowest-price tenders, in the recognition that the value of the project to the organisation is far more than just the out-turn cost of the project, and includes the capital and revenue costs over the estimated life of the project. It is well known in the construction industry that lowest-priced tenders do not necessarily equate to best value for money and in fact may result in larger and more frequent management problems on the project resulting from claims. Furthermore, the appointment of a contractor on a value-for-money basis is likely to reduce the risk of project failure.

> Value for money includes non-price items as well as price.

Value for money means assessing the optimum balance of the whole-life cost cycle, construction cost, performance, time and quality to meet the client's requirements. Some aspects of a tenderer's proposals that might be considered (beyond the tender price itself) include

- acquisition costs
- procurement and head office costs
- ease of maintenance and operational performance costs
- management, operating and disposal costs
- innovation requirements, durability and adaptability
- the out-turn quality and the time taken to complete the project
- information about the tenderer's organisation (e.g. organisational structure)
- the tenderer's supply chain management
- the tenderer's relevant previous experience
- how the tenderer intends to manage the resources on site, quality, and health and safety on site
- how the tenderer would respond to a described situation
- corporate social responsibility with economic, environmental and social sustainability factors
- and, of course, the health and safety plan, the programme, method statement, design proposal, financial robustness, environmental policy, list of subcontractors, and other contract-specific items.

The tender evaluation process should recognise not only the tender price of the tenderer's proposals but the other aspects of the proposal that are likely to contribute to the achievement of overall value for money (see the above list).

Communicating a value-for-money approach to tenderers during the tendering process may also discourage prospective tenderers from attempting to 'buy' jobs (in the hope of later turning a profit through the issuing of claims).

1.3. The procurement process

The procurement process for works projects (Figure 1.1) typically involves the following steps:

1 **Define the need**.
   Identifying and clearly defining the business need.
2 **Establish the budget**.
   Obtaining the necessary funding for the planned expenditure.
3 **Agree the procurement strategy**.
   Discuss with relevant parties and agree the procurement strategy for the overall project.
4 **Establish the project team**.
   - *Appoint consultants*
     Procuring the services of external consultants for feasibility/design (if required) (which involves a separate procurement exercise).
   - *Establish the contractor input*
     Commencing discussion with contractors (if required) (using an appointment) for initial comments on design, buildability and so on.
5 **Develop the requirement (brief)**.
   Developing the scope of the work (or the client's requirements if a design-and-build approach is to be adopted) is crucial for managing a value-for-money approach. An initial risk assessment would also be undertaken at this time.

Figure 1.1 The procurement process

```
┌─────────────┐   ┌─────────────┐   ┌─────────────┐   ┌─────────────┐
│ Define need │──▶│ Establish   │──▶│ Agree       │──▶│ Establish   │
│             │   │ budget      │   │ procurement │   │ project team│
│             │   │             │   │ strategy    │   │             │
└─────────────┘   └─────────────┘   └─────────────┘   └─────────────┘
                                                              │
                                                              ▼
┌─────────────┐   ┌─────────────┐   ┌─────────────┐   ┌─────────────┐
│ Prepare     │◀──│ Invitation  │◀──│ Finalise    │◀──│ Develop     │
│ evaluation  │   │ to tender   │   │ contract    │   │ brief       │
│ model       │   │ (ITT)       │   │ strategy    │   │             │
└─────────────┘   └─────────────┘   └─────────────┘   └─────────────┘
       │
       ▼
┌─────────────┐   ┌─────────────┐   ┌─────────────┐   ┌─────────────┐
│ Issue ITT   │──▶│ Receive     │──▶│ Tender      │──▶│ Negotiation │
│             │   │ tenders     │   │ evaluation  │   │             │
│             │   │             │   │ and         │   │             │
│             │   │             │   │ clarification│  │             │
└─────────────┘   └─────────────┘   └─────────────┘   └─────────────┘
                                                              │
                                                              ▼
                  ┌─────────────┐   ┌─────────────┐   ┌─────────────┐
                  │ Contract    │◀──│ Award       │◀──│ Award       │
                  │ management  │   │ contract    │   │ recommendation│
                  └─────────────┘   └─────────────┘   └─────────────┘
```

6   **Finalise the contract strategy.**
Discussing the contract strategy, taking into account the wider procurement strategy, the completeness/status of the scope of the work and the requirements of the client specific to the contract in terms of delay damages, retention and so on.

7   **Prepare tender documentation (invitation to tender).**
Producing tender documentation and identifying the tender list (prospective tenderers), and drafting contract documentation.

8   **Prepare the evaluation model.**
Developing the tender evaluation model and considering the necessary range of value-for-money criteria. This model should contain the commercial: non-commercial weighting. Each descriptor under each of the commercial and non-commercial aspects should also be weighted for scoring purposes.

9   **Issue the invitation to tender.**
Issuing the invitation to tender letter with the accompanying tender documentation (ensuring that the conditions of tendering are separated from what will eventually become contract documentation).

10   **Receive tenders.**
Receiving the tenders and formally logging them.

11   **Tender evaluation and clarification.**
   – Evaluating tenders in terms of commercial and non-commercial aspects (e.g. technical, quality and sustainability). Ideally, the technical evaluators do not receive priced tenders. For some traditional contracts, the commercial manager may be required to check the prices submitted by the tenderers and provide an evaluation report.
   – Clarification of elements may be formally sought if required (and before evaluation can be finalised).
   – Establishing a shortlist or identifying the preferred bidder if this is clear.

12   **Negotiation.**
Carrying out negotiation (if required; and in accordance with public procurement regulations where applicable) with the shortlist or the preferred bidder.

13   **Award the recommendation.**
Compiling the contract documentation using the tender documentation issued at the invitation to tender stage and adjusting it, taking into account any proposals and changes at the negotiation stage. Seeking formal authority to award a contract based upon this final set of contract documentation.

14   **Award the contract.**
Issuing the contract documentation in duplicate original to the contractor for their signature and countersigning documents on their return. One fully executed original should then be returned to the contractor as their copy of the contract.

15 **Contract management**.

The contract management process then takes over. This includes post-project evaluation and, ultimately, post-occupancy review (where applicable). Monitoring and reviewing the process (for procurement and project delivery) to facilitate continuous improvement.

1.4. The procurement time cycle

It is important whenever possible to leave sufficient time during the procurement process to ensure that the required procedures, process and policies can be followed, especially where public procurement rules apply. In some instances, execution of the full process will not be possible: for example, emergency or safety-related works. In addition, it is advisable to establish an accelerated procurement process that can be adopted where there is a critical operational need.

Generally, the time cycle for the procurement process should be measured back from the intended date for completion or operation of the project to determine the necessary starting time for the procurement process (Figure 1.2).

Figure 1.2 The procurement process timeline

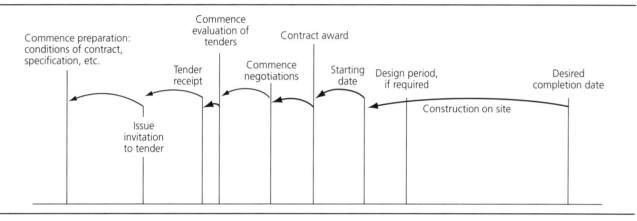

Clearly, reasonable estimates as to the appropriate time allowances allocated for each stage of the procurement process activities need to be made. If the value of a UK public works project is greater than its EU threshold, the procurement will be subject to public procurement regulations, the time periods for certain activities will be dictated, and any key dates should be incorporated into the procurement time-frame. The key dates might by legislation be the date for prospective tenderers registering interest and the final date for tender return.

Allowing insufficient time for the procurement process will inevitably result in inadequate time being left for concluding the process – for example, evaluation and contract drafting – and could jeopardise the quality of the contract that is achieved.

> Leave adequate time for procurement in the project programme.

It is often early on, in the procurement stages of the project, where the greatest benefits can be derived – and, in recognition of this, the ECC secondary Option X22 facilitates early contractor involvement. Benefits might include obtaining better value for money or improved quality, reducing time, or ensuring that a particularly important issue is properly addressed. Good preparation can greatly enhance performance during and on completion of the project – like many things in life, the greater the effort expended initially, the greater the rewards.

1.5. The procurement strategy

An important part of any procurement strategy is recognising the parameters under which the strategy operates. Not only will there be internal policies and procedures to follow regarding the issuing of tender documentation and ensuring auditable processes also but there are also legal, statutory and regulatory requirements to follow.

1.5.1 What is the procurement strategy?

A procurement strategy involves looking at the longer-term, wider procurement picture (such as long-term agreements) for an organisation, rather than merely considering the current contract (the subject of a procurement strategy cannot be fully discussed here, and is mentioned only to emphasise that clients should consider a view that is not confined to the on-site construction time of one contract). A contract or series of contracts may be stepping-stones to the achievement of a broader procurement or business objective.

UK public procurement regulations require certain public procurement bodies to publish a procurement strategy providing specified information and to report on it regularly. In general, a procurement strategy involves considering

- whether the contract is just one of many that make up a larger programme of work
- how the project fits in with overall business activity; that is,
  - how many other projects are being constructed on the same site, affecting interfaces, resources and cost analysis if the site set-up is shared
  - how many other projects are ongoing or due to commence in the organisation and which may require use of the same resources
- how the procurement activity required for the project fits into the organisation's overall procurement activity plan:
  - for example, the organisation might already have arrangements in place with specialist suppliers or subcontractors or might consider procuring separately the concrete required for a large building project and free-issuing it to the contractor, if it considers that this would prove more economic than having the contractor source it.

1.5.2 The procurement route

A narrowed view of procurement strategy for a contract could include considering the procurement route that will be adopted for the contract; that is, how is it best to procure the contract?

- using any existing framework contractors (see section 1.9 below)
- using a two-stage tender process
- how early in the procurement process to involve the contractor; that is, before the design stage, during the design stage or only at the build stage?

1.6. The contract strategy

The contract strategy contains the details chosen for the particular project. This should take place after the procurement strategy has been decided upon and implemented, since the overall procurement strategy affects the way in which the contract is procured.

> - The procurement strategy considers the wider impact on the business.
> - The procurement route for a contract includes considering how to procure that contract.
> - The contract strategy includes deciding what the contract will include (liquidated damages, retention, bonus for early completion, etc.).

The contract strategy involves deciding how the conditions of contract used help you to achieve the objectives of the project.

- Do you need retention?
- Do you need delay damages?
- Do you want to take over parts of the work as they are completed?
- How do you want to pay the contractor?

You may also want to consider the following as part of the contract strategy:

- With whom do you wish design responsibility to lie (with the design team or the contractor)?
- Who will take responsibility for project delivery?

Most of these questions are answered through the choices made in the Contract Data (see Chapter 3 on completion of the Contract Data).

1.7. Public sector procurement

In the background of any procurement in the UK public sector lie public procurement regulations (currently applicable to UK public authorities and utilities only). Any procurement should follow legislative requirements, the exclusion, selection and award criteria, and the procedures referred to in the contract notice, standstill procedures and the requirements for an award notice.

> The EU procurement directives affect only public bodies and utilities.

Procurement in the public sector is tightly regulated, and auditability and public accountability must be ensured at all times. The procurement process is often more detailed and involved than that of the private sector.

The procurement process in the public sector must ensure

- a clear audit trail
- the ability to demonstrate clearly that value for money has been achieved
- that compliance with all applicable regulations/statutory and legal requirements has been met at all times.

1.8. Generic good principles for effective procurement

The principles of procurement for any project are the same. This section is therefore aimed at providing a reminder and overview of some of the golden rules to apply when preparing documentation for procurement purposes, so that some of the pitfalls that befall procurement activities can be avoided.

The tender documents should be originated specifically for each project. Any temptation to copy or amend previous similar projects should be resisted, as this may lead to the occurrence of anomalies and inconsistencies resulting from some or all of the following:

- Using previous specifications that have not been updated or that include irrelevant information.
- Using previous specifications that have been amended to suit the previous contract. (It may be that previous conditions of contract or paragraphs in the specification were introduced by a project manager who had been affected by their lack in the past. These conditions can be onerous and draconian or may simply not be suitable for all contracts or all contractors.)
- Using the same conditions of contract as were used in previous contracts, without considering how appropriate they are to the current project.
- The inclusion of every possible document in the filing cabinet to 'cover' you and make sure that nothing has been left out, rather than considering the appropriateness of the document. This will almost certainly lead to a confused contract with duplication or conflict between the documents.
- Including conditions of tendering and tender terminology throughout the document (rather than confining them to a document for conditions of tendering; tender terminology should not be included in specifications, in the client's requirements or in the conditions of contract): for example, that the tenderer is to include a programme with their tender, that the tenderer is to have taken all information about the site into account when tendering, that the tenderer is to have included all items in their pricing.

1.8.1 Letters of award

It is the practice of many clients to issue a letter of award to the successful tenderer. This letter states that the tenderer's offer has been accepted, and that the contract 'includes the following'. The list that ensues includes the tender documentation, the tenderer's offer, any subsequent offers, and communications and minutes of meetings in which anything relevant to the contract appears.

Because there are elements of the tender documentation, such as the rules of tendering, that do not form part of the contract document, it is inadequate simply to state in the letter of award that the contract comprises the tender documentation, the tenderer's offer, and all communications up to a particular date. This potentially introduces conflicts, ambiguities and a source of disputes that could be avoided very easily. Conflicts between the tender documents and the tenderer's offer may result, and confusion arises as to which prevails. For this reason, it is advisable to include an order of precedence in the letter of acceptance. However, if a dispute were to occur, it might still be extraordinarily difficult to ascertain, among all the paper that makes up the contract, what the contract actually says and in whose favour the dispute may lie. Even if an order of precedence is stated, the contractor might have a good reason for stating that their tender was not made on the premise argued by the client.

The more work that is invested prior to contract award and in drafting contract documents that are concise, accurate and relevant, the more aware the client will be of exactly what they are contracting for.

A letter of award should simply state that the contractor has been awarded a contract. The entire contract should then be attached, and should include all the documents that comprise the contract. The 'entire document' in this sense does not mean a copy of the tender and any other communications but, rather, means a copy of the documents that make up the contract, as amended for any changes made in the tender and other communications. The tender documentation and the tenderer's offer **in their entirety** are not part of the contract, although some of the documents within them will form part of the contract, including

- the form of contract/articles of agreement, completed and available for signing
- the conditions of contract, amended as agreed between the parties
- the final prices as negotiated between the parties
- the definitive specification (or the client's requirements and the contractor's proposal for a design-and-build contract)
- a contractor's programme submitted at the tender stage.

In this way, both parties know what the contract comprises, and this sets the basis of the entire contracting relationship, including the obligations of the parties to one another.

1.8.2 Letters of intent

Letters of intent are complicated and potentially leave one of the parties unprotected. Issuing a letter of intent should be avoided if at all possible. The client should never be in a situation where, in order for the work to start, a letter of intent has to be issued because the contract is not in place. Procurement should take place with an efficiency that allows the contract to be in place before the work is required to start.

1.9. Long-term agreements
1.9.1 A manageable supply base

Many organisations consider their spend on a project-by-project basis. Separate teams are arranged for each project, and there is continuity in the spend only to the extent that the same bidders might continually win work. Figure 1.3 represents this procurement strategy.

The organisation's ability to drive strategic improvements is facilitated by moving away from a project-by-project focus to a business and programme focus (Figure 1.4).

Organisations with a business and programme focus take project delivery seriously and do not consider cost, time and quality drivers in isolation. Provided the organisation can think

Figure 1.3 Project-by-project focus

Figure 1.4 Business/programme focus

strategically, it has the opportunity to manage its supply chain more effectively. By taking a programme approach to the business spend, the group of projects is considered together and the supply chain can be consolidated to facilitate working more effectively with a reduced and more manageable group of suppliers. The most obvious way to do this and to prove value for money is to put in place long-term agreements. In this way, the team can work together to achieve the targets.

1.9.2 Continuous improvement

Procurement is a costly operation that is critical to the overall success of a business. A key driver for businesses, whether in the private or public sector, is to improve the quality of the product or service and to drive out waste, unnecessary costs in machinery, materials, labour, procedures and practices. In terms of construction, this has seen a focus on driving out waste in the procurement of works, goods and services. A useful vehicle through which continuous improvement of this nature can be achieved is the long-term agreement.

> Procurement is a critical business activity.

1.9.3 Long-term agreements

A long-term agreement is where the parties agree to focus on long-term business improvements for the client's organisation. Examples of the benefits sought are

- a reduced construction period (increased speed to market)
- an enhanced safety environment/culture
- assurance of supply (including availability when required and of the standard required)
- improved reliability (project delivery on time, to cost and quality)
- reduced costs through familiarity and increased efficiency of delivery
- better-quality solutions achieved over time
- efficiency of working (process improvements, faster learning, and increased productivity over time).

The parties are able to do this through working in partnership over a prolonged period. This also improves contractor understanding of the client's business, the procedure and the types of solutions required. By working under a long-term agreement, continuous improvement targets can be set against a range of criteria, and a sustained effort made to meet these.

Examples of the potential benefits that might be realised (and for which targets could be set) include the following:

- Workload security: for example,
    - continuity of workload/planned programmes of work (security of work in a recession)
    - relationship continuity and development, such as
        - continuity of people/skills/competencies/expertise
        - economies of scale
        - improved product and services (e.g. investment in new technology/techniques)
        - consistency of approach
        - securing skills and scarce resources (e.g. skill shortages in an overheating marketplace either generally or for specialist skills).
- Enhanced relationship with the contractor, leading to a partnering attitude and a unified approach to the work being done.

Figure 1.5 The economic cycle

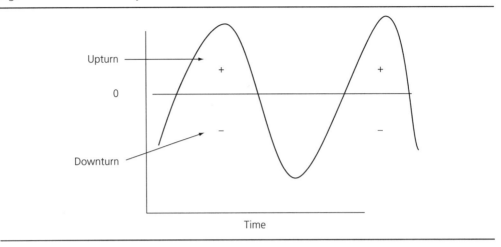

Figure 1.6 Features of the economic cycle

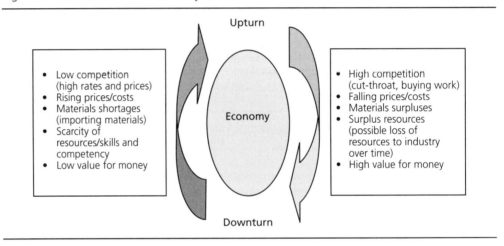

- ■ Contribution of ideas and designs that would assist the client in their business.
- ■ Marketplace/economies of scale.
- ■ Less wasteful tendering.
- ■ More trusting relationships.

The benefits sought obviously depend on many factors, including market conditions, market trends, business objectives and so on. Figures 1.5 and 1.6 show some of the influencing factors. There is a distinct difference between best practice procurement and the optimisation of procurement (economics, principles and climate).

Long-term agreements should take a flexible view that is not dependent on the climate; that is, a view that does not take advantage of recessions in the economy (Figure 1.7).

Figure 1.7 Vision versus view

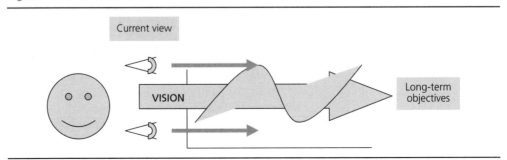

This could involve

- not including liquidated damages in the contracts, since a long-term view is being taken
- not including retention, since retention indicates a short-term view
- encouraging innovation in the marketplace even when times are tough
- considering the benefits of an upturn and a downturn
- seeing through to the long term – vision versus view.

1.10. How does the ECC contribute to effective 'partnership'?

The ECC inherently accommodates the latest vogues for partnering, long-term agreements, alliances, frameworks and the like. The procedures that the ECC uses can be seen to lie in a similar or indeed 'back-to-back' fashion with 'partnering'. Some of these can be categorised as follows.

1.10.1 Contract administration

- Addresses problems as and when they occur.
- An effective communication tool that awakens responsibility. The ECC encourages people to communicate; it proposes sanctions upon *Contractors* or *Project Managers* who fail to perform diligently.
- Smooths the way to focusing on real issues and progressing the job.
- Compensation events are a risk-levelling device not allowing hidden costs and avoiding tail-end claims.
- A quotation procedure that allows flexibility at the discretion of the contract parties.

1.10.2 Dispute resolution

- Internal resolution, adjudication as a first step in lieu of arbitration or litigation, and the choice to use an independent board to resolve disputes.
- The joint appointment of dispute resolvers.

1.10.3 The *Client's* contribution

- Through the *Project Manager*, decision-making is not left entirely to designers or architects.
- As the contract should not be left in the 'bottom drawer', the *Client* is forced to address real issues and take an active involvement in their project's maturation.

The contract recognises that the *Client*, having expressed a desire to enter into the contract, has to maintain responsibility under it and so via their *Project Manager* must take an active role in its performance.

1.10.4 Multiplicity of use

As a set of interlocking documents, the ECC allows uniformity and consistency across a full spectrum of contract types, for example building, civil engineering and professional services. This ability to interlock has a crucial benefit for 'partnerships', and is explored in a little greater depth in the next section.

1.10.5 Trust

By the very fact that a client is prepared to adopt the ECC, they are sending out a clear signal to prospective contractors and consultants that their attitude has changed. It is a statement or declaration of intent to which we must all respond.

> The ECC embodies many aspects of partnering.

1.10.6 The suite/family of contracts

The ECC offers the potential to encompass the majority of procurement and project routes through its main and secondary Options. NEC4 Design Build and Operate increases this flexibility.

1.11. The ECC tendering procedure

The ECC tendering procedure is represented diagrammatically in Figure 1.8 and discussed in the following subsections.

1.11.1 General

When issuing an invitation to tender letter and tender documentation, the most important thing to remember is that these documents will form the basis of the resulting contract. The tender documentation should not be incorporated into the contract by reference, but should be redrafted to become the contract. In other words, the tender documents should not be listed

Figure 1.8 The ECC tendering procedure

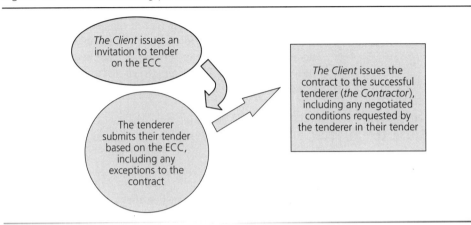

in the contract award letter as part of the contract: they should be drafted in such a way that parts of them can be discarded and not form part of the contract.

Similarly, the tender should not be incorporated into the contract by reference. Those parts of it that amend the tender documentation should be extracted, and the contract amended accordingly.

Many clients will consider a redraft far too much work. It may be that for smaller contracts, where the risks are lower, the work required for a redraft could exceed the benefits in terms of consistency and lack of ambiguity. It might be considered worth the effort of getting into a routine of general amendment, however. In whatever manner the client chooses to issue the contract – whether through redraft or whether by total inclusion of all tender and post-tender documentation – the client should ensure that ambiguities and inconsistencies are removed from the document in order to decrease the potential for conflict.

> The tender documentation should not be incorporated into the contract by reference, but should be redrafted to become the contract.

1.11.2 The *Client's* requirements

The tenderer will submit a compliant bid for the *works* based on the tender documentation (Contract Data, Scope and Site Information, etc.) sent to them by the *Client*. The original tender documentation may be changed by the *Client* during the tendering period by the issuing of amending letters. This will form the basis of the information upon which the tenderer's price is based.

These requirements will form the basis of the *Contractor's* obligations under the contract. Care should be taken to ensure that any amendments or qualifications made by the *Contractor* as part of their submission are clearly identified. In these instances, unless the *Client* had indicated that variant bids were acceptable, the *Contractor* will have submitted a non-compliant bid.

1.11.3 The *conditions of contract*

Any amendments to the *conditions of contract* suggested by the tenderer and agreed to by the *Client* should be incorporated into the contract by redraft rather than by reference. A reference to a letter or the tenderer's bid, where the redrafted condition appears, could cause confusion and conflict, particularly if the amendment is not in an obvious and easily accessible place. If the *Client* accepts the change, it is more effective to include the change in a noticeable place.

1.12. From tendering to contract

It can be seen from the example below that the invitation to tender forms the basis of the contract. Although the invitation to tender may comprise different elements, the items listed below will be, in general, included.

The **tender** documents comprise the following:

- Part A:
  - letter of invitation
  - conditions of tendering
- Part B:
  - tender submission document
- Part C:
  - form of contract/articles of agreement
  - Contract Data
  - contract prices
  - Scope
  - Site Information.

The **contract** comprises the following:

- award letter
- form of contract/articles of agreement
- Contract Data parts one and two
- contract prices
- Scope
- Site Information.

The following gives a brief explanation of Parts A to C of the tender documents.

- Part A: the part of the tender documents that describes the conditions of tendering and the instructions to tenderers. This part is not included in the resulting contract.
- Part B: the part of the tender documents that relates to how the tenderer is to respond; that is, the form of tender and the schedules they are to complete such as curricula vitae (CVs), project organisation charts, the health and safety policy, a programme and the method statement (statement of how the *Contractor* plans to do the work). This part is not included in the contract, although the response submitted by the tenderer incorporating this part could be included in the contract.
- Part C: the part of the tender documents that forms the basis of the contract; that is, the *conditions of contract*, the *Client's* requirements and the agreement that will be signed between the *Client* and the successful tenderer. There should be no reference in this part to the 'tender' or the 'tenderer'.

The items that are specifically related to tendering (Parts A and B) should be kept in one part of the tender documents. Parts A and B do not form part of the eventual contract, and can be detached and removed when pulling the contract together.

There should therefore be no reference to the tender or tenderers in the *Client's* requirements or any other document that will form part of the contract (Part C). There should only be reference to the *Contractor* – the person who will ultimately be responsible for carrying out the work.

1.12.1 The structure of an ECC invitation to tender from the *Client*

A possible structure for ECC tender documentation is as follows (see Appendix 1 to this chapter for an example of the invitation to tender format):

- letter of invitation
- conditions of tendering
- tender submission documents detailing what the tenderer is to include with their tender (e.g. a statement of how the *Contractor* plans to do the work)
- form of contract/articles of agreement
- Contract Data part one (completed)
- Contract Data part two (left blank – to be completed by the tenderer)
- contract prices (blank form to be completed by the tenderer)
- Scope and Site Information.

1.12.2 The structure of an ECC tender from the *Contractor*

A possible structure for a tender based on the ECC is as follows:

- letter from the tenderer
- tender submission documents completed
- Contract Data part two (completed)
- contract prices (completed)
- compliance with the Scope, or the tenderer's proposal where it is a design-and-build or performance specification.

1.12.3 The structure of an ECC contract

A suggested structure for a contract based on the ECC is as follows:

- form of contract/articles of agreement
- Contract Data parts one and two
- Contract prices (*activity schedule* or *bill of quantities*)
- Scope
- Site Information.

This is the simplest way to present a contract using the ECC. The form of contract/articles of agreement is a written document that facilitates the signature of both Parties and states the Parties' principal obligations; that is, that the *Client* will pay the *Contractor* for the work done in accordance with the contract; and that the *Contractor* will carry out the *works* in accordance with the contract.

The form of contract/Articles of agreement is a mechanism for contract execution. It is part of a bound contract document where the rest of the contract is exactly as agreed between the Parties; that is, the documents have been amended to reflect any changes made during the tendering process.

Where the *Client* does not choose this mechanism, they are likely to use a contract award letter accepting the tender sum as stated in the form of tender and listing the documents that are included in the contract, such as

- the invitation to tender
- the tender
- the outcome of any post-tender negotiation.

As stated above, however, this particular method may introduce potential disputes unnecessarily and too early in the project life cycle.

1.13. Procurement scenarios

1.13.1 Introduction

The following scenarios are examples of some of the procurement routes available to *Clients*:

- The *Client* has fully designed the required *works* and requires a lump sum price from the *Contractor* for the construction of the *works*.
- The *Client* has provided a performance specification to the *Contractor* and requires them to design and construct the *works* on a fixed sum basis.
- The *Client* requires the *Contractor* to design and construct the *works* and to participate in a target cost contract.
- The *Client* requires immediate and urgent *works* that are not designed.
- The *Client* requires a feasibility study to be completed, a working up of the specification and the construction of the *works*.

The choice of ECC main Option is based on the completeness of the Scope, as well as on the informed decision of the *Client*. In general, there is no need to use anything other than an Option A contract, where the design is fully developed by the *Client's* designers or the *Contractor* and the work is not urgent.

Where the work is designed by the *Client*, the completeness of the design (and possibly other factors, such as the incentivisation of the *Contractor*, past relationships (frameworking) and the current climate and situation financially, politically, etc.) will determine whether Option A/B or

C/D is used. The use of Option C or D is a choice made by the *Client* according to whether the scope can support a fixed price or not. In other words, where the Scope is defined sufficiently to support an Option A contract, then Option A would be the payment option that would minimise the *Client's* risk. Despite this robustness of the Scope, the *Client* could still choose Option C if they wished to amend the risk and flexibility structure of the contract and embark on a target cost contract.

Target cost contracts are often chosen for the wrong reasons or for inappropriate situations. Target cost contracts do not always provide an incentive to the *Contractor*, and the *Client* is often left to pay far more than budgeted because of the target cost mechanism. Similarly, in situations where the design is fixed, whether by the *Client* or the *Contractor*, a fixed-price contract is often more appropriate as a method of payment. Cost-reimbursable contracts are useful where the design is uncertain, and where a target cost contract would result in burdensome administration. In general, if the *Client* is uncertain of the scope of their own design, then there will be additional costs, and a target cost mechanism may not reduce those costs.

1.13.2 Scenario 1 – *works* designed, fixed price

Where the *Client* has previously engaged a designer to prepare the *Client's* requirements for a contract, and now requires a fixed price for providing the works, there are few steps involved in the procurement cycle.

Where the *works* are designed fully, the most appropriate payment route to adopt is that of a priced contract. This could be achieved using the ECC as Option A or B. Option B provides for the use of a *bill of quantities*, where a remeasurement route is chosen by the *Client*. Option A uses an *activity schedule* (milestone payment schedule) as the tool for payment to the *Contractor*, and is therefore a lump sum form of contract.

The steps in the procurement cycle are as follows:

1. Develop the *Client's* requirements through to a completed design (could be an internal appointment).
2. Check that the *Client's* requirements integrate with the *Client's* own special requirements.
3. Draft the contract and tender documentation using Option A or B (could be an internal appointment).
4. Draft the method of evaluation of the tender.
5. Issue the invitation to tender letter and accompanying tender documentation.
6. Evaluate the returned tenders on the basis of the Prices and the Schedule of Cost Components.
7. Commercially and contractually assess the tenders based on the method of evaluation.
8. Place the contract (in accordance with the award criteria included in the invitation to tender or in any *Official Journal of the European Union* (*OJEU*) notice for public sector and utilities procurement).

1.13.3 Scenario 2 – *works* to be designed by the *Contractor*, fixed price

Where the *works* are to be designed by the *Contractor*, a fixed-price contract is still appropriate; however, the *Client* might prefer to use a target cost contract for other reasons. The procurement process is likely to be a one- or two-stage process in order to ensure that the most appropriate contractor against certain predetermined criteria is chosen. Whatever procurement route is chosen, the route should be spelled out in an *OJEU* notice (where this is required in accordance with the financial thresholds for a works contract for public sector bodies or utilities) and adhered to at all times.

A two-stage route could be chosen where there is insufficient time to develop the design in the tender period or where the *Client* does not want the tenderers to bear the costs inherent in each of them developing a design. It should be noted that this route could result in greater *Client* risk where a preferred contractor is chosen to develop the design. This is because the competitive tendering aspect is lost, and therefore the criteria for determining the best design are undermined and commercial risk is increased.

1.13.3.1 The one-stage process

A one-stage process might be used in conjunction with a value engineering process where the scope of work is partly uncertain. The process is based on a robust set of *Client's* requirements from which it is possible to tender a fixed price.

The steps in the procurement cycle are as follows:

- Develop the *Client's* requirements.
- Draft the contract and tender documentation using the chosen Option.
- Draft the method of evaluation.
- Issue the invitation to tender letter and accompanying tender documentation for a design-and-build contract.
- Evaluate the tenders on the basis of the Prices and the Schedule of Cost Components as determined by the evaluation model.
- Determine the technical acceptability of the tender design.
- Commercially and contractually assess the tenders.
- Place the contract (in accordance with the award criteria included in the invitation to tender or in any *OJEU* notice for public sector and utilities procurement).
- Develop and commence the value engineering exercise to develop the design.
- Notify and instruct a quotation for a compensation event to embrace the results of the value engineering exercise.

1.13.3.2 The two-stage process

Where the *works* are to be designed by the *Contractor*, a fixed price is generally the most appropriate method of payment throughout. This may be achieved using the ECC as Option A. Option A uses an *activity schedule*, or milestone payment schedule, as the tool for payment to the *Contractor*.

The steps in the procurement cycle are as follows:

- Develop the *Client's* requirements.
- Draft the contract and tender documentation using the chosen option.
- Draft the method of evaluation.
- Issue the invitation to tender and accompanying tender documentation for a design-and-build contract.
- Evaluate the tenders on the basis of the Prices and the Schedule of Cost Components or the Short Schedule of Cost Components as determined by the evaluation model.
- Determine the technical acceptability of tender design.
- Commercially and contractually assess the tenders.
- Draft an NEC4 Professional Service Contract for the development of the design by the *Contractor*, using Option A. The question of who owns the design should be answered using the contract conditions. This contract is finalised and executed to allow the *Contractor* to develop the design. The final output of this contract is a design and an offered sum for providing the *works* in accordance with the design. There are alternatives to this procurement route (see below).
- A contract for the *works* is also drafted and executed, but note the reduced legal and commercial viability of such a contract (see the discussion in scenario 2 above (Section 1.13.3)).

An alternative to engaging the *Contractor* on two contracts, one the Professional Service Contract for the design of the *works*, and the other the ECC for the construction of the *works*, is to contract with the *Contractor* using only the ECC contract. There are advantages and disadvantages for both these methods as detailed below.

1.13.3.3 Using both the Professional Service Contract and the ECC

Advantages	Disadvantages
■ The method of payment can be a fixed price throughout	■ Slightly more work is involved in drafting two contracts instead of one; however, the work involved in shoehorning a works contract to fit design and construction could turn out to be considerably more
■ The *Client* has more power in negotiating the price for the works contract	
■ The *Client* can choose not to continue with the works contract	■ The *Contractor* may be uncertain of receiving the construction contract, which may increase the price overall
■ The works contract can still be drafted to include the design as belonging to the *Contractor*, thereby preserving the *Client's* contractual position	
■ Using two contracts clearly sets out the Parties' contractual positions and allows the use of a more appropriate contract for the design of the *works*	

1.13.3.4 Using the ECC with secondary Option X22

Advantages	Disadvantages
■ Where a target cost contract is chosen for the design and construction, procurement is initially easier	■ The target cost will have to be revised once the design is complete, and the new target either negotiated or devised using compensation events, resulting in a clumsy attempt to work backwards
■ The negotiation of the Price for the works contract could be intense since the *Client* is already contracted with the *Contractor* and there is little room to manoeuvre	■ Two different payment options could be chosen to cope with the two different aspects of the contract: design (Option A) and construct (Option E to be amended to Option A once phase 1 is complete). This results in negotiation and work to be completed part way into the contract
■ Secondary Option X22 (early *Contractor* involvement) sets out how the Price is to be determined and provides for a notice to proceed between stages 1 and 2.	

The ECC can be used for design-and-build contracts.

1.13.4 Scenario 3 – *works* to be designed by the *Contractor*, target cost

Where the *works* are to be designed by the *Contractor*, a fixed price is generally the most appropriate method of payment throughout. There could be times, however, when, for reasons of their own, or due to the uncertainty of the *Client's* performance specification or the uncertainty of other conditions impacting on the works, the *Client* might choose to use a target cost contract. This could be achieved using the ECC as Option C.

Option C uses an *activity schedule*, or milestone payment schedule, to ascertain the *Contractor's* target cost; that is, what the *Contractor* thinks the *works* will cost if the described Scope does not change. This target cost is amended throughout the contract when compensation events occur. The *Contractor* is paid their Defined Cost plus Fee throughout the period of the contract. The total of these payments is compared with the target cost at Completion, and the difference is shared out between the *Client* and the *Contractor* in a predetermined manner. The share mechanism is therefore intended to be an incentive to the *Contractor* to maximise their part of the share, but the *Client's* risk is increased.

In this case, the procurement decisions and actions are the same as for those of a fixed-price contract, except that Option A/B becomes Option C/D.

1.13.5 Scenario 4 – *works* to start immediately without the *Client's* requirements

Where work is required to start urgently with little idea of scope, an Option E contract is the most appropriate option. If the contract for a public body or utility is large enough to be subject to EU procurement regulations, then competitive tendering is still required, increasing the time period before a contractor can commence. In some instances an accelerated procedure may be used. It could be that a call for competition could be dispensed with if it is strictly necessary for reasons of extreme urgency and the reasons that brought about the event were unforeseeable by the *Client*.

Otherwise, there are the following steps in the procurement cycle:

■ The contract is drafted with a brief description of requirements.
■ The *Client* holds discussions with various contractors to decide on the contractor to do the work, or a contractor is chosen through knowledge of previous works and industry experience.
■ A contract is finalised through negotiation and evaluation.

1.13.6 Scenario 5 – feasibility study, design and build

It is not appropriate to use the ECC for all three stages of this procurement strategy. Some clients might choose to use the ECC including Option X5 (sectional completion); however, it is likely that consultants will be engaged for the feasibility study and possibly the design aspect, and therefore the use of one contract for two different contractors is not advised. Even if a contractor were to be engaged for all three items, by the very nature of a feasibility study, the design-and-build stage might not be undertaken if such a project is not deemed to be feasible.

It is more appropriate to engage a consultant using the NEC4 Professional Service Contract for the feasibility and design stages, and then to engage a contractor using the ECC after an invitation to tender (if required) using the design written by the consultant. An alternative is to engage a consultant using the Professional Service Contract for the feasibility stage and then a contractor on the ECC for the design-and-build stage.

> It is not appropriate to use the ECC for feasibility, design and build using sectional Completion unless secondary Option X22 is selected.

1.13.7 Conclusion

Note that the scenarios presented above are simply that – scenarios. They do not form recommendations, and they are not set in stone. They are provided simply as a means to convey the various decisions that *Clients* could face.

Procuring an Engineering and Construction Contract
ISBN 978-0-7277-6184-2

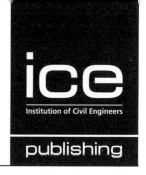

Appendix 1
Assessing tenders

Synopsis

This appendix provides suggestions for assessing tenders, including

- what to ask for in the invitation to tender
- what should be submitted with the tender
- what the primary commercial and technical documents are
- what to consider in conducting the evaluation.

A1.1 Introduction

Part of procurement is deciding how you will assess the tenders that are returned and what information you require and in what format you require it. All the normal aspects of assessing tenders exist with the ECC; there are, however, a few areas that need careful consideration.

Selecting the right contractor is very important. Public bodies and utilities are required to adhere to the EU procurement directives. Organisations that are not required to follow the EU procurement directives could still benefit from some of the guidelines and principles contained within them.

The assessment criteria should be based on your objectives for the project in both technical and commercial terms. These will in turn affect how you set up the tender documentation in the first place and what information you will call for at the time of tender.

A1.2. Information to include in the invitation to tender

The invitation to tender should include all the information that you will need to assess tenders. This means asking for information to be included in the tender that will help you make your decision. It also means telling the tenderer how you intend to evaluate the tender, so that they are able to give you what you need to make your evaluation.

A1.2.1 Information required from the tenderer

The invitation to tender should list the information required from the tenderer. Such information could include the following (see also Section A2.5 of Appendix 2 to this chapter), and should be clearly separated into selection criteria and award criteria (especially for EU procurements):

- Contract Data part two.
- A programme that shows how the tenderer intends to Provide the Works, including any statement of how the *Contractor* plans to do the work and resource statement. The programme could take various forms depending on the project, the main Option chosen and how the *Client* wants to approach the project. For example, a *Client* who has a set Completion Date but wants to test the tenderers' programming performance could ask for an outline programme with milestones only, but a detailed ECC programme for one aspect of the *works* on the critical path that will allow differentiation between tenders.
- An organisational chart showing how the *Contractor* is set up to deal with quality management or environmental issues.
- Information about the people who will be working on the contract, such as extracts from the CVs showing qualifications and experience particularly related to the project.
- Pricing information showing breakdowns relevant to the programme.
- Environmental, economic and social sustainability information, including community benefits and supported businesses.
- Health and safety issues.
- Details about past projects.
- Design innovation where design is an important part of the Scope.
- A method statement for a particular part of the *works* rather than the whole of the *works*.
- The tender price and an evaluation of the Schedule of Cost Components (including the Short Schedule of Cost Components) for cost-based options C, D and E.
- The partnering approach and philosophy, for projects that incorporate Options X12 and X22.

This imposes a discipline to think about the evaluation of the tenders before the invitation to tender letter and accompanying tender documentation are issued. It also facilitates the request for the information that will enable evaluation.

A1.3. Evaluation
A1.3.1 General

Some clients like to split the evaluation of tender submissions into technical and commercial parts. In such situations, each of these elements of the tender will be delivered at the same time, but will be in separate packages to be reviewed on a technical and commercial basis in isolation from each other. A reason for separating the technical and commercial elements of the tender is so that the technical reviewers are not influenced by price. Figure A1.1 shows some of the factors that influence the assessment of tenders.

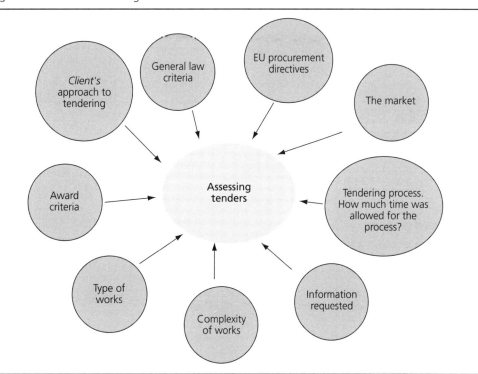

Figure A1.1 Factors affecting the assessment of tenders

A1.3.2 Information submitted with the tender

The following is a list of the types of information that may be requested and submitted with a tender (see also Appendix 2).

Commercial:
1   form of tender
2   *activity schedule* or *bill of quantities* (pricing document)
3   Contract Data part two
4   requested alternative prices or options
5   ultimate holding company guarantee/bonds (e.g. performance bond or advanced payment bond)
6   design warranties for *Contractor* design
7   collateral warranties
8   insurance certificates.

Technical (note that some of the following are selection criteria and some are award criteria; the two sets of criteria should be separated and addressed separately in the tender documentation):

9   CV of *key persons*
10   organisational structure
11   health and safety plan
12   quality assurance plan
13   programme
14   Scope provided by the *Contractor* for their design
15   statement of how the *Contractor* plans to do the work
16   design of Equipment
17   names of proposed Subcontractors.

This list is made on the basis of a one-stage tender. Where a pre-qualification stage has already been evaluated, there will be no need to request information such as financial statements and statements of previous experience on similar projects, including referees, since these would have been submitted at the pre-qualification stage.

The *Project Manager* should look out for any qualifications in the covering letter or within the tender documents submitted together with any proposed alternatives and so on.

Table A1.1 Example tender evaluation matrix

Tenderer 1					
Evaluation criteria	Weighting, B	Requirements	Score: 0 to 10 (low to high), A	Comments	Weighted score, $\frac{A}{100} \times B$
Technical					
1 Relevant experience	4.0		8.0	Good recent experience on similar projects	0.32
2 Technical capability	20.0		9.0	Innovative design solutions	1.80
3 Programme	5.0		7.0	Some logic incorrect	0.35
5 Subcontractors	3.0	Specify what you would expect to see from the tender so that you are able to mark all the tenders in the same way	6.0	Quality of Subcontractors generally low	0.18
6 Risk management	5.0		2.0	Little consideration given to risk	0.06
7 Quality plan	5.0		7.0	Well presented; information incomplete	0.35
8 Health and safety plan	10.0		7.0	Well presented	0.7
9 Environmental issues	3.0		5.0	Not given enough consideration	0.15
10 Organisational structure and key persons	2.5		7.0	Good structure that should marry well with our own team	0.17
11 Partnering philosophy	2.5		8.0	Good ethos and outlook	0.2
Commercial					0.0
12 *Activity schedule/ bill of quantities*	30.0	Specify requirements	9.0	Robust pricing – no qualifications – all data completed. Competitive pricing	2.7
13 Model compensation event to evaluate percentages	10.0		7.0		0.70
Total weighting	100.0				
Total score			82.0		
Total weighted score					7.68
Rank based on weighted score			3		

A1.3.3 Evaluation criteria It is important to ensure that all the tenders are given due consideration and that a robust tender evaluation process is put in place. Table A1.1 shows a typical example of an evaluation matrix, and it shows some of the criteria upon which a *Client* may wish to evaluate a tender. (Note again that some of the evaluation criteria listed in the table are selection criteria and some are award criteria. The two sets of criteria should be separated and addressed separately rather than approached together as shown in Table A1.1.)

Figure A1.2 Example evaluation matrices for the entries made in Contract Data part two by the *Contractor*

Tender assessment pro forma

Schedule of Cost Components

1 Equipment purchased for work on the contract, with an on cost charge are

Equipment	time-related on cost charge		per time period	
[insert description]	....		[time period]	=
[insert description]	....		[time period]	=
Subtotal			=	£ ....

2 Rates for special Equipment

Equipment		rate		
[insert description]		rate	=	
Subtotal			=	£ ....

3 Manufacture and fabrication

Total number of hours to be divided equally between each tendered category = 100 hours

	Hours		Rate	Total	
Category 1	....	at			
Category 2	....	at			
Category 3	....	at			
Category 4	....	at		‾‾‾‾‾‾	
Subtotal				= £ _____	= £ ....

4 Design

Total number of hours to be divided equally between each tendered category = 100 hours

	Hours		Rate	Total	
Category 1	....	at			
Category 2	....	at			
Category 3	....	at			
Category 4	....	at		‾‾‾‾‾‾	
Subtotal				= £ _____	= £ ....

5 *fee percentage* ....%   = £ ....

Total of compensation events   = £ ....
Total for tender assessment   = £ ....

6 Other factors
- Completion Date (value to *Client* for every week of time saving)
- Technical ability
- Health and safety
- Quality
- Design

All evaluations are relative to the other tenders; that is, a tender is evaluated as being competitive or not against the backdrop of the market as represented by the tenderers.

With each criterion, you should detail what you are looking for, so that comparisons against the tenderers are made against the same requirements. It is also possible to list requirements as 'essential' and 'desirable' so that those tenderers who do not state that they are capable of providing the items deemed to be essential are dropped from the evaluation.

A1.3.3.1 Commercial evaluation

The important commercial documents in a tender are as follows:

- Contract Data part one
- *activity schedule* or *bill of quantities*

Figure A1.2 Continued

Tender assessment pro forma

Short Schedule of Cost Components

1 *people rates*

Category of person		Unit	Rate		
[insert description]					
[insert description]					
Subtotal				= £	

2 Percentage adjustment for Equipment
   % (state plus or minus)

3 Rates for other Equipment

Equipment			rate		
[insert description]			rate =		
Subtotal				= £	

4 Design

Total number of hours to be	*Hours*	*Rate*	*Total*		
divided equally between each					
tendered category = 100 hours					
Category 1	....	at			
Category 2	....	at			
Category 3	....	at			
Category 4	....	at			
Subtotal			= £ _____	= £	

5 *fee percentage*   ....%   = £ ....

Total of compensation events   = £ ....
Total for tender assessment   = £ ....

6 Other factors
   • Completion Date (value to
     Client for every week of
     time saving)
   • Technical ability
   • Health and safety
   • Quality
   • Design

■ Contract Data part two where the *Contractor* inserts key commercial data, for example:
  – Schedule of Cost Components
    ○ *fee percentage*
    ○ Equipment rates
  – Short Schedule of Cost Components
    ○ *people rates*
    ○ Equipment – percentage for adjustment
    ○ *fee percentage*.

Figure A1.2 is an example of an evaluation matrix for the entries made in the Contract Data part two by the *Contractor*. For this sort of assessment, the assumptions should be clearly stated, such as the number of hours to be used, or the values on which percentages are to be based. A 'model compensation event' is generally the best way to consider this element of the evaluation. The data for the Schedule of Cost Components can be a large part of the tender evaluation, particularly for Options C, D and E; therefore, careful thought should be given to the assessment of these data.

A1.3.3.2 Technical

The important technical documents in a tender for the purposes of evaluation include

■ the Scope provided by the *Contractor* for their design

- the programme
- the statement of how the *Contractor* plans to do the work and resource schedules
- the quality plan.

Figure A1.2 is an example of an evaluation matrix for the entries made in Contract Data part two by the *Contractor*.

A1.4. Conducting the evaluation

The following is a list of items for the *Project Manager* to consider on receipt of a tender (note again that some items are selection criteria, and the two should be addressed separately and not together as indicated in this list):

- The *activity schedule* is not used to assess change but is more of a cash flow document. Therefore, you need to check for front loading of early activities. It should be remembered that early cash flow may reduce the *Contractor's* finance charges and may enable them to offer a commercially advantageous tender.
- *Key persons* – what are the qualifications and experience of the proposed people?
- Programme – how well has the *Contractor* understood the requirements of the *Client*? Does the programme include all the information requested in the invitation to tender and tendering instructions? Does it have any implications for the *Client*; that is, does it include dates by which the *Client* must provide information or 'free issue' materials or do something?

The following is a list of items for the *Contractor* or Subcontractor to consider on submitting a tender:

- Always ensure that you have fully completed Contract Data part two. Inserting 'non-applicable', 'n/a', 'to be advised' or simply leaving blanks will lead to problems later when you come to discuss compensation events with the *Project Manager*.
- Remember that the information given in Contract Data part two will be used by the *Client* to assess your tender and will be used as noted above to assess the effects of change.
- The names and details of *key persons* will also be used by the *Client* to assess your tender.
- The *activity schedule* (Option A) can be thought of as a milestone payments schedule. You are only paid for these activities when they are complete, so they may have to be broken down into a number of activities or sub-activities to suit monthly valuations.
- Your *fee percentage* should be realistic and show an understanding of how it will be used.

Procuring an Engineering and Construction Contract
ISBN 978-0-7277-6184-2

ICE Publishing: All rights reserved
http://dx.doi.org/10.1680/pecc.61842.029

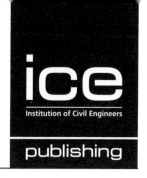

Appendix 2
ECC tender documentation

Synopsis

This appendix provides suggestions for the invitation to tender and ECC tender documentation, including

- the letter of invitation
- conditions of tendering
- tender submission documents
- Contract Data
- contract prices
- the Scope
- Site Information.

A2.1. Introduction

In general, the invitation to tender and tender documentation should include the following:

- the header page of the contract (including the name of the *Client*, the project/contract number and a description of the *works*)
- an invitation to tender letter
- conditions of tendering
- a list of tender submission documents – a description of items that the tenderer is required to include with their tender for evaluation purposes
- the draft form of contract/articles of agreement
- Contract Data parts one and two
- contract prices
- the Scope
- Site Information.

A2.2. The header page

The header page could include

- the name of the *Client*
- the description of the *works*
- the project title
- the project number
- the contract number
- the date.

A2.3. The letter of invitation

The letter could include the following:

- A heading line ('Invitation to Tender for [the *works*]').
- A statement inviting the tenderer to submit a tender to Provide the Works.
- A statement that the attached documents describe how the tenderer is to submit their tender.
- A statement that a tender submission in response to this invitation to tender is deemed to be acceptance of the tender procedures and the *conditions of contract*.
- The name and contact details of the person responsible for issuing the tender documentation.
- The tender return date and time.

A2.4. Conditions of tendering

Standard conditions of tendering should be included here.

Examples of elements for inclusion are included below; however, these are examples only, and should not be read as obligatory inclusions for an ECC contract. If the ECC invitation to tender letter and tender documentation you are issuing are required to take into account the EU procurement directions, some adjustments may need to be made.

A2.4.1 General

This section could include the following:

- The name and contact details of the person responsible for the invitation to tender.
- The return date and time for the tender.
- A statement that all communication should be in writing.
- A statement that the tender documents at all times remain the property of the *Client*. The invitation to tender and any associated correspondence are subject to the laws of copyright and must not be reproduced, whether in whole or in part, without the prior written consent of the *Client*.
- A statement regarding the confidentiality of the invitation to tender and the tender. This is particularly important for the UK public sector, bearing in mind the Freedom of Information Act 2000.
- A requirement for the tenderer to acknowledge receipt of this enquiry within three working days, clearly stating the intention to accept or decline the invitation. If the invitation is declined, the tenderer should return all the tender documents, which must be treated with total confidentiality, with the acknowledgement. Different procedures may be described for e-sourcing.
- A statement that the tenderer will bear all costs associated with the preparation and submission of their tender.

A2.4.2 Documentation to be submitted by the tenderer

This section could include the following:

- A list of the tender documentation included in the invitation to tender.
- A statement that the tender documentation may be modified by the *Client* prior to the tender return date. Any procedures describing the issuing of addenda should be included as well (e.g. the tender should acknowledge the addendum and the tenderer may ask for an extension of time to the tender return date).
- A statement regarding the acceptability or otherwise of alternative tenders, how this should be effected and any restrictions on the basis of an alternative tender (e.g. different completion date or technical method).

A2.4.3 Preparation of tenders

This section could include the following:

- A statement that the tenders should be submitted in the *language of the contract*.
- A statement that the tenderer should become familiar with all aspects that could affect the price submitted.
- A statement that the prices should be based on the whole of the *works*.
- The validity period of the tender (e.g. 60 days).
- A procedure for dealing with queries (e.g. a time limit on when they can be received, to whom the answers will be given, and that all queries and answers should be in writing).

A2.4.4 Tender submission

This section could include the following:

- Description of the e-sourcing system used.
- For paper returns:
  - the number of copies of the tender required to be submitted
  - how the tenders should be presented (e.g. in separate envelopes with no markings to indicate the name of the tenderer)
  - whether faxed or emailed copies of the tender will be accepted
  - how late tenders will be dealt with (e.g. returned unopened).

A2.4.5 Evaluation of tenders

This section could include the following:

- A statement regarding the *Client's* obligations regarding the tender process (e.g. the *Client* may accept any tender, cancel the tender process, reject all tenders without any obligation to inform the tenderer of the reason for such action, abandon the work or issue another invitation to tender for the same or similar *works* at any time).
- A statement regarding how the *Client* will award the contract (e.g. the *Client* does not undertake to accept the lowest tender in respect of the invitation to tender; or the *Client* will award the contract on the basis of the most economically advantageous tender in terms of quality of service (weighting %), speed of service (weighting %), technical ability (weighting %) and experience of individuals (weighting %) proposed, together with the method statement (weighting %) as well as the anticipated price (weighting %)). (Note that some of the criteria listed are selection criteria rather than award criteria, and should be addressed separately by the evaluation team and not altogether as indicated in this list.)

A2.4.6 The evaluation process and post-tender negotiation

This section could include the following:

- A statement that the *Client* may enter into contractual negotiations with selected shortlisted tenderers with the intention of entering into a contract with a selected tenderer. The statement could add what this process would entail (e.g. presentation and discussion by the tenderer at a chosen site and/or a meeting at the tenderer's premises to discuss the proposal further and to meet selected personnel).
- A statement that the *Client* may specify additional requirements or agree detailed conditions of contract as appropriate to the specific requirement with the selected tenderer(s) at any time prior to formal contract award.
- A statement that the contract resulting from the invitation to tender may not be exclusive.

A2.4.7 Formation of the contract

This section could include the following:

- the process of notifying tenderers when the evaluation has been completed
- a statement that unsuccessful tenderers are required, on request, to return all the invitation to tender documents, including any drawings, supplied for the preparation of the tender
- a statement about how the contract will be formed (e.g. the *Client* will issue duplicate original contract documents to the successful tenderer as confirmation of the award of the contract; or the execution of the contract will be deemed to have taken place when a tender submission and a letter of acceptance have been exchanged between the Parties)
- a list of items that are required prior to contract award (e.g. any collateral warranties and guarantees required; any parent company guarantees and bonds required; and the policies and certificates for insurance to be provided)
- the process for informing tenderers of the successful contractor and any debriefing offered to unsuccessful tenderers.

A2.4.8 Contract aspects

This section is optional, and could include the following:

- A statement that a particular number of days' notice of commencement of site work will be given by the *Project Manager*.

A2.5. The tender submission documents

This section includes the forms and documents that the *Client* requires the tenderer to submit with their tender, and could include the following (note that some of the items listed are selection criteria not award criteria, and so should be addressed separately and not all together as indicated in this list):

- the form of tender (including a statement that the *conditions of contract* are accepted)
- a declaration of bona fide tender (if deemed necessary)
- a declaration of site visit (if deemed necessary)
- a list of proposed Subcontractors
- samples of materials
- working hours for site construction work (these may have already been stipulated in the Scope)
- the project organisation/management structure, together with CVs of key personnel
- the health and safety policy and health and safety plan
- documentary evidence that the *Contractor* is complying with the Construction (Design and Management) Regulations 2015 (the CDM Regulations)
- industrial relations policy
- Control of Substances Hazardous to Health Regulations 2002 assessments in respect of any hazardous substances used by the *Contractor* for the *works*, whether on or off the site
- the quality plan
- the programme
- a statement of how the *Contractor* plans to do the work
- the *Contractor's* proposal (Scope provided by the *Contractor* for their design)
- design of Equipment
- haulage routes
- design management
- the environmental policy
- risk management.

A2.6. Contract documents

The next sections are those documents that would be included in any contract resulting from the invitation to tender. The documents would include

- the form of contract/articles of agreement
- the Contract Data
- the contract prices
- the Scope
- Site Information.

A2.6.1 Form of contract/ articles of agreement

A form of contract/articles of agreement document has not been included in this appendix. Each organisation will have its own standard document that should be tailored to suit the ECC terminology. This form could be used to state the Contract Date, which does not appear in other ECC documents.

A2.6.2 Contract Data

The Contract Data should be included next. Contract Data part one by the *Client* should be completed prior to issue, and the choices required to be made in Contract Data part two by the *Contractor* should have been made by the *Client* prior to issue. See Chapter 3 for a complete listing of the Contract Data entries for the *Client* and the *Contractor*.

A2.6.3 Contract prices

The *activity schedule* or *bill of quantities* is included here; an example of each is given below. However, these should be preceded by the following:

1 Preamble to the *activity schedule/bill of quantities*
2 Introduction.

The total of the Prices is fully inclusive for the whole of the *works*, and includes all aspects that the *Contractor* is required to do to Provide the Works in accordance with the contract.

Include here instructions for completing the *activity schedule*.

Note that it is not necessary to include lists of things that the Prices should include. The Scope should make it quite clear what the *Contractor* is to provide, and therefore they should know what they are to price for. In the past, contractors might have said that they had not priced for something because it had not been detailed in the bill or other payment mechanism. In the ECC, this is a spurious argument. Note that the *bill of quantities* or the *activity schedule* is not the Scope.

3a *Activity schedule.*

Activity number	Description of activity	Lump sum price: £
1		
2		
3		
	Total of the Prices	

or

3b *Bill of quantities.*

Number	Description	Rate	Unit	Quantity	Lump sum price: £

A2.6.4 Scope

Insert the Scope here (including the form for ultimate holding company guarantee and performance bond). Guidelines for the drafting of the Scope and what should be included in the Scope are included in Chapter 4.

A2.6.5 Site Information

Insert the Site Information here. Guidelines for the drafting of Site Information and what should be included in the Site Information are included in Chapter 4.

Procuring an Engineering and Construction Contract
ISBN 978-0-7277-6184-2

Chapter 2
Contract Options

Synopsis

This chapter looks at the Contract Options available within the ECC, including

- ECC main and secondary Options
- priced contracts
- target contracts
- cost-reimbursable contracts
- choosing a main Option
- choosing a secondary Option.

2.1. Introduction

The main and secondary Options chosen, together with the core clauses, form the terms and conditions applicable to the contract. The choice of main and secondary Options is therefore very important in determining how the *Contractor* is to be paid, where and how the financial risks of the project lie, and what some of the other project risks are.

The Options chosen by the *Client* form part of the contract strategy for the project. The choice of Options should be reviewed with every contract, rather than simply choosing the same Options that were used in previous contracts. Most contracts tend to have different risks associated with them and different requirements, so that a mix of Options may be more appropriate than opting for the same format every time.

These principles apply equally to contractors and subcontractors when setting up their own contracting strategy.

2.2. ECC main and secondary Options – general

There are six main Option clauses (A–F) within the ECC, each of which represents the way in which the *Contractor* will be paid during the period of the contract, as illustrated in Table 2.1.

Table 2.1 Main Options (payment mechanisms) in the ECC

Contract type	Main Option	Price document
Priced contracts	A B	*Activity schedule* *Bill of quantities*
Target contracts	C D	*Activity schedule* *Bill of quantities*
Cost reimbursable	E	Defined Cost
Management contract	F	Defined Cost

In addition to the six main Options, there are 21 secondary Options (Table 2.2), which are subject to some restrictions: Option X1 (price adjustment for inflation) may not be used with Options E and F; Option X3 (multiple currencies) may only be used with Options A and B; Option X16 (retention) may not be used with Option F; Option X20 (Key Performance Indicators) may not be used with Option X12; and Option X22 (early *Contractor* involvement) may not be used with Options A, B, D and F. In addition, there are three dispute resolution procedure options in the ECC, one of which is required to be chosen: Option W1 is used where adjudication is required unless the Housing Grants, Construction and Regeneration Act 1996 (HGCR Act) applies, Option W2 is used where the HGCR Act does apply and Option W3 is chosen when a Dispute Avoidance Board is to be used.

Option X19 is not used in the ECC.

The contract document is operational without any of the secondary Option clauses. These are bolt-on provisions that enable each *Client* to select provisions in accordance with their individual needs.

Among the secondary Options available are several provisions that in traditional standard forms of contract would be within the main body of clauses, such as retention and delay damages.

The primary part of the contract strategy is therefore formed by the selection of main and secondary Options and dispute resolution procedure options (Figure 2.1).

2.3. Main Options
2.3.1 The choice of main Option

Some of the choices are easy:

- If you want a management contractor, choose Option F.
- If you want a cost-reimbursable contract, choose Option E.
- If you want to use a *bill of quantities*, choose Option B or D.

Table 2.2 Secondary Options in the ECC

Secondary Option[a]	Title
X1	Price adjustment for inflation (used only with Options A, B, C and D)
X2	Changes in the law
X3	Multiple currencies (used only with Options A and B)
X4 (changed title)	Ultimate holding company guarantee
X5	Sectional Completion
X6	Bonus for early Completion
X7	Delay damages
X8 (new)	Undertakings to the *Client* or Others
X9 (new)	Transfer of rights
X10	Information modelling
X11	Termination by *Client*
X12 (changed title)	Multiparty collaboration (not used with Option X20)
X13	Performance bond
X14	Advanced payment to the *Contractor*
X15 (changed title)	The *Contractor's* design
X16	Retention (not used with Option F)
X17	Low performance damages
X18	Limitation of liability
X20	Key Performance Indicators (not used with Option X12)
X21 (new)	Whole life cost
X22 (new)	Early *Contractor* involvement (used only with Options C and E)
Y(UK)1	Project Bank Account
Y(UK)2	The Housing Grants, Construction and Regeneration Act 1996
Y(UK)3	The Contracts (Rights of Third Parties) Act 1999
Z	*Additional conditions of contract*

[a] Comments in brackets: change in NEC4 from NEC3.

- If you want to use an *activity schedule*, choose Option A or C, which describes milestone payments.
- If you want a priced contract, choose Option A or B.
- If you want a remeasurement contract, choose Option B.
- If you want a target contract, choose Option C or D.

The selection of a main Option determines the balance of financial risk between the *Client* and the *Contractor*, as summarised in Figure 2.2. It should also be borne in mind that the objective of a contracting strategy may only be achievable through a combination of the above Options. For example, if early *Contractor* involvement is required, then secondary Option X22 can be selected, but this limits the main Option that can be chosen because secondary Option X22 can only be used with main Options C and E. In other situations it may be the case that the combination may require the use of the NEC4 Professional Service Contract, where the *Contractor/* Subcontractor is being asked to be involved at an early stage in design development with the *Client*.

It should also be noted that the *Contractor's* and/or Subcontractor's own subcontracts do not necessarily require them to be 'back to back'. For example, the *Contractor* or Subcontractor may be on an Option C contract, but they can have subcontracts let on Option A.

Some clients in partnering/framework arrangements require the *Contractor's* or Subcontractor's own contracts to be 'back to back'; for example, if the *Contractor's* contract is Option C, then the Subcontractor's contract should also use Option C. This often occurs where the client wishes to see a flow down through the supply chain of incentivisation on a project. Stating your

Figure 2.1 The ECC contract structure

Figure 2.2 Balance of risk for each main Option under the ECC

Contract type	Main Options	Balance of risk	
		Client	*Contractor*
Priced	A		
	B		
Target	C		
	D		
Cost reimbursable	E		
Management contract	F		

partnering approach/philosophy and how you intend to approach incentivisation of your own supply chain are often questions asked as part of the tendering process.

> A *Contractor* appointment on an Option C target cost with an *activity schedule* contract does not necessarily have to have an Option C subcontract. Unless, of course, it is a requirement of the *Client's* contract.

The choice of main Option also affects the *Contractor's* incentive and the flexibility enjoyed by the *Client* during the contract. Fixed-price contracts tend to increase the risk to the *Contractor* and decrease the risk to the *Client*. Fixed-price contracts also require a more fixed scope, however, and consequently the *Client* has less flexibility available to them. In addition, if the fixed scope has to change because it was not properly defined, the *Client's* risk increases. The

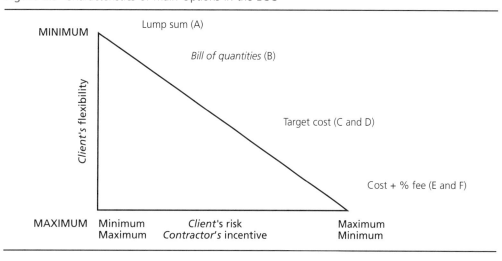

Figure 2.3 Characteristics of main Options in the ECC

graph in Figure 2.3 shows the flexibility, risk and incentive patterns that characterise the types of contracts available within the ECC.

Following the principle that risk should be placed with those best able to manage it, the choice of main Option could depend on the quality of the Scope and Site Information available at the tender stage. Put simply, a *Contractor* faced with poor-quality information while tendering for a priced contract may include a significant allowance for risk. In these circumstances the *Client* will subsequently pay the *Contractor* the tendered sum whether or not the risk arises. Where the scope of work is poorly defined, the *Client* is well advised to select a cost-reimbursable option, as by doing so they will pay only if the risk occurs.

Other factors influencing the choice of main Options include where an *Client* might feel that a target contract could result in a more open relationship with the *Contractor* and that successive contracts using Option C could result in a price reduction through the use of incentives (using Option C even when the scope is clear may facilitate a more open and beneficial relationship).

Many clients tend to prefer priced contracts (Options A and B – note that Option B is not a fixed-price contract in the same way as Option A, since Option B is fully remeasurable), where the budget for the contract is relatively secure, barring variations ordered by the *Client* or their representative. In order to receive a fixed-price contract from a *Contractor*, however, the scope of works is required to be well defined and fixed. This is often not possible. In this case, the *Client* has a decision to make about whether they want to take the risk of changes made to the contract, or whether they want to share the risk with the *Contractor*, who could make valuable contributions to the solving of buildability and design issues. This could change their choice of main Option from A to C or from B to D.

In some cases, a *Client* may have an idea about what a target contract (Options C and D under the ECC) represents. Some clients may regard a target contract as a means of 'sharing the risk'. This is, of course, an aspect of any target contract, but there are other considerations as well. Principally, the behaviour of the two Parties to the contract should be modified from the arm's length attitude of a fixed-price contract to the more collaborative relationship that is required to make a target contract work.

A primary driver for the choice of main Option under the ECC is the quality and standard of the Scope available. The Scope describes the *Client's* requirements. An Option A contract based on a Scope that is only 50% complete may give rise to numerous changes that will change the profile of the contract from a fixed-price low-*Client*-risk contract to a variable-price and therefore higher-risk contract.

2.3.2 Trade-offs in choosing a main Option

The choice of main Option can also depend on the trade-off between cost, time and quality (Figure 2.4). For example, a contract for which the point in the triangle is close to the time apex

Figure 2.4 Project management trade-off between cost, time and quality

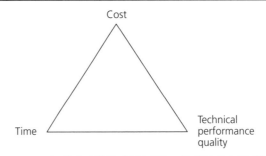

could mean that the time of completion (e.g. new buildings for the Commonwealth Games or shops/retail outlets) or the starting time (e.g. annual factory shutdowns or limited working windows) is more important than the price. This does not mean that price is **not** important, rather that time is more important, and therefore price-bound Options such as A and B might not be the appropriate choice in this situation.

It is vital to choose the right main Option in the first instance. Problems could arise where a main Option is chosen that does not match the completeness of the Scope or other parts of the contract strategy. Where there are so many compensation events occurring on an Option A contract that the *Project Manager* is struggling to keep abreast of them all, this may be an indication that the Scope is incomplete and that the contract should have been an Option C/D or E contract.

The following are factors that should be taken into account when deciding which main Option to choose:

- Who has the necessary design expertise? (This could affect the main Option under the assumption that Options A and B are designed by the *Client*; however, a design-and-build contract could be completed using Options A or B with a few adjustments.)
- Is there a particular pressure to complete quickly? (Pressure to complete quickly would usually lead to an Option E contract.)
- How important is performance of the completed *works*?
- Is certainty of final cost more important than lowest final cost? (Pointing towards an Option A contract rather than Option C.)
- Where can a risk best be managed? (The *Contractor* carries more financial risk in Options A and B and less risk in Option E.)
- What total risk is tolerable for contractors?
- How important is cross-contract coordination to achievement of project objectives? (In this case, Option C, D or E would be more suitable.)
- Does the *Client* have good reasons for selecting specialist contractors or suppliers for parts of the *works*?

The clarity of the *Client's* objectives is important in choosing the correct main Option for the project. It is not possible to achieve all of certainty of price, certainty of completion date, the ability to change the works, reallocating risk to the *Contractor*, retaining design responsibility and lowest price. It is important to ensure that the specification is correct where there is *Client* design.

> Risk should be placed with those best able to manage it.

2.4. Priced contracts

There are two priced Options available in the ECC:

- Option A – a priced contract with an *activity schedule* (where the *Contractor* is paid on completion of activities)
- Option B – a priced contract with a *bill of quantities* (a remeasurable contract).

2.4.1 Option A – priced contract with *activity schedule*

An *activity schedule* (the Activity Schedule as defined in Option A) is a list of activities prepared by the *Contractor* that represents the activities they expect to undertake in carrying out the *works*. In traditional contracts, these activities might have been called milestone payments.

2.4.1.1 A1: tender

Option A requires the tenderer to tender lump sum prices against the *activity schedule*. The Prices are the lump sums attached to each activity, and the total of the Prices is the contract sum.

If the *Contractor* is given a wholly free hand to produce the *activity schedule*, this could make it difficult for the *Client* to evaluate tenders, where each tenderer submits an *activity schedule* containing different activities (where the invitation to tender letter and accompanying tender documentation were part of a competitive tender exercise). If the *Client* is overly prescriptive in the detailing of the *activity schedule*, this could affect the *Contractor's* cash flow, where the *Client* has not detailed a sufficient number of activities.

In an attempt to find a balance between the two, some *Clients* include guidelines or state requirements on the minimum level of breakdown for the *activity schedule* or activities within it in much the same way as a contract sum analysis or work breakdown structure. This enables the *Client* to identify significant items of work or stages of work that they are particularly interested in or concerned about and enables these items to be clearly identified, and also facilitates greater ease of comparison between tenderers during tender evaluation. Such requirements should be detailed in the instructions to the tenderers at the time of tender.

For example, the *Client* could draw up a list of primary activities that will form the basis of their evaluation exercise, and instruct the tenderers to price these activities and any other sub-activities they wish to add that make up the primary activities. For example, the *Client* could list the following as primary activities in the *activity schedule* where the *works* is an office building: access routes, foundations, floor, walls, roof and fit-out.

A counter-argument to all the above is that the *Contractor* prepares the *activity schedule* because a *Contractor* may be able to offer a commercially advantageous tender through the structuring of payments due for completed activities.

The *activity schedule* in its purest form is an opportunity for the *Contractor* to structure their payments and cash flow to suit their requirements and be able to offer the benefit of this through their tender to the *Client*.

Concerns are often raised in relation to the front loading of early activities by the *Contractor*. Some clients, especially those with budgetary constraints on yearly spend, are interested in and may seek options/alternative prices from tenderers where they are able to offer them early or up-front payments for work subject to certain conditions outlined in *additional conditions of contract* in an Option Z clause.

2.4.1.2 A2: risk

Because Option A is a lump sum contract, there tends to be more risk allocated to the *Contractor* than to the *Client*. The *Contractor* is paid for their work based on the lump sum prices tendered against the *activity schedule*. It therefore carries the risk for accurate pricing for the contract overall (in just the same way as they would in any other lump sum contract), and its cash flow is based on the allocation of the lump sum price against each activity in the *activity schedule*.

2.4.1.3 A3: payment

Under Option A, the *Contractor* is paid for activities that are complete at each assessment date. The amount to be paid is the amount entered by the tenderer against that activity in the *activity schedule* (as amended for compensation events).

There are two points to note here. The first is that the activity is required to be complete by the assessment date if it is to be included in the amount due. This means that the *Contractor* could have programmed and included the activity so that it would meet an assessment date. Any change in the programme could therefore affect this programme and the *Contractor's* cash flow. The second is that an activity is complete when it has reached completion in accordance with the

Figure 2.5 Activities spanning assessment dates

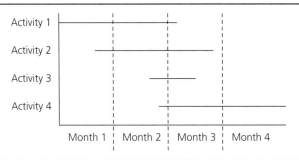

contract. In general, this definition will be included in the Scope and should be objective enough for the *Project Manager* to decide when the activity is complete. (For a fuller description of Completion, see Chapter 1 of Book One and Chapter 2 of Book Three.)

It is therefore important that the duration of activities described is not so long that they span assessment dates, since the completed activities are assessed at each assessment date. In Figure 2.5, activity 1 will be assessed as complete at the end of month 3, and will therefore be paid at the end of month 4 (or thereabouts). The *Contractor* will be required to finance this cash flow from the beginning of the project until the end of month 4 – a heavy burden. Activities 2 and 3 will also be assessed as complete at the end of month 3, and activity 4 will be assessed when it is complete.

A balance needs to be struck between

- the contractual requirement for each activity to be represented in the programme
- the need to ensure that there should not be so many activities that the programme becomes cumbersome and too onerous to be revised/reviewed every month.

In Figure 2.6 there are many activities that may prove a challenge to manage, but cash flow is assured.

The most effective solution is to programme activities so that they can be completed before an assessment date. There may be situations where it is necessary to amend the definition of the Price for Work Done to Date in clause A11.2(29) to allow for percentages of activities completed, so that the correct balance of the number of activities in the programme and *activity schedule* is achieved (Figure 2.7).

Figure 2.6 Activities too small to be included in the programme

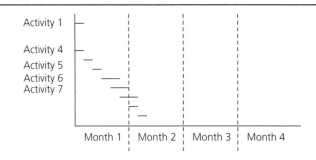

2.4.1.4 A4: compensation events

In theory, few changes should take place in an Option A contract since it supposedly has a well-defined scheme of works and is a lump sum contract. Small compensation events could still occur, however. In this case, the assessment for any compensation events that are implemented will be added to the lump sum price of the relevant activity, thereby increasing the total of the Prices. The payment taking place on completion of that activity will therefore be the tendered lump sum adjusted for compensation events.

Figure 2.7 Activities designed to suit the assessment dates

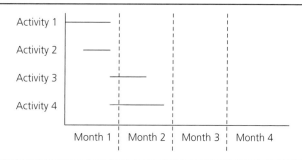

Compensation events are priced using the Short Schedule of Cost Components (clause 11.2(23)). A rate or lump sum may also be used to assess a compensation event instead of Defined Cost (clause 63.2).

A compensation event may delay completion of an activity so that completion occurs one or more assessment dates later than the *Contractor* planned at the tender stage. This could affect the *Contractor's* cash flow, since payment for that activity could be a month or more later than expected.

Consideration should also be given by the *Client* and *Contractor* to any work being identified as a **new activity** that would de-link the completion of this additional/extra work from the completion of the whole activity.

Compensation events are priced using only the Short Schedule of Cost Components rather than the *activity schedule*. It is important, therefore, that the *Contractor* completes the data for the Short Schedule of Cost Components in Contract Data part two. In the past, some tenderers have left this section blank, thinking that if it is a lump sum contract there is no requirement to provide data for the Schedule of Cost Components (the theoretical ramifications of this are that the *Contractor* carries out compensation events for free, since no data have been provided or inserted by the *Contractor*). In this instance, there could be room for negotiation (although the *Project Manager* could refuse because the Parties have already entered into contract); and certainly disagreement between the Parties. It is more effective and expedient for the *Client* and *Contractor* to ensure that these data have been completed in the first place.

2.4.1.5 A5: selection

A fuller discussion of the aspects to be taken into account when choosing a main Option is included in Section 2.2 above. In general, Option A should be selected by the *Client* when

- the Scope is complete (does not necessarily imply correct)
- a firm price and low risk are more important than flexibility.

2.4.2 Option B – priced contract with *bill of quantities*

A *bill of quantities* is a list of work items and quantities with the unit of measurement as stated in a *method of measurement*, and which describes the items to be included and how the quantities are to be calculated.

2.4.2.1 B1: tender

Option B requires the tenderer to tender rates and prices against each item included in the *bill of quantities*. The *bill of quantities* is usually prepared by the *Client*. The sum of all products (rate × quantity) is the total of the Prices.

2.4.2.2 B2: risk

Option B is a priced contract; therefore, there tends to be more risk allocated to the *Contractor* than to the *Client*. The *Contractor* is paid for their work at the prices tendered against the *bill of quantities*, and therefore they carry the risk of having priced the items correctly, although they do not carry the risk of changes in quantity.

Some *Clients* have amended Option B contracts so that the *Contractor* is to price for the risk associated with changes in quantities. This amendment effectively makes it a lump sum priced contract like Option A, but using a *bill of quantities*.

2.4.2.3 B3: payment

Option B is a remeasurable contract. The *Contractor* is paid for the actual quantity of work completed, as identified in the *bill of quantities* multiplied by the rates and prices against each of these items.

Because the *Contractor* is paid according to what they have completed in the period up to the assessment date, there is no requirement for completion of activities as there is with Option A.

2.4.2.4 B4: compensation events

Compensation events are priced using the Short Schedule of Cost Components rather than the *bill of quantities*, although if both Parties agree, a rate or lump sum may be used by agreement to assess a part of a compensation event instead of Defined Cost (clause 63.2). The default position (of pricing compensation events using the Short Schedule of Cost Components) is to overcome the problems associated with re-rating or star rates for *bill of quantities* items. It is aimed at preventing the *Client* being disadvantaged where the quantities in the *bill of quantities* were incorrect and some loading of the *bill of quantities* has taken place. It also protects the *Contractor* from the *Project Manager* insisting on inappropriate rates and prices in the *bill of quantities* being used to assess the cost implications of the change.

As with Option A, it is important, therefore, that the *Contractor* completes the data for the Short Schedule of Cost Components in Contract Data part two.

Note that there are three extra compensation events (clauses B60.4, B60.5 and B60.6) in Option B, that recognise it is a remeasurable contract and that the final remeasurement at the end of the contract might reveal inconsistencies that apply retrospectively.

2.4.2.5 B5: selection

A fuller discussion of the aspects to be taken into account when choosing a main Option is included in Section 2.3 above. In general, Option B should be selected by the *Client* when

■ a firm price is required but some changes in quantities may occur
■ the *Client* or their professional team wishes to use a *bill of quantities*
■ a schedule of defined works or services is required.

2.5. Target contracts
2.5.1 Adjustment of the target price (Options C and D only)

A target price contract works as follows. At the tender stage the *Contractor* assesses the cost of doing the defined work in the same way that they would under any other contract arrangement. Having added their fee for overhead and profit and made any other tender adjustment in the usual way, the price they arrive at and submit with their tender constitutes the target price – or the 'total of the Prices' as the ECC refers to it (not to be confused with the definition Total of the Prices in Option D, which is used as a comparison with the Price for Work Done to Date for the purpose of calculating the *Contractor's* share). Depending on whether Option C or D is used, the total of the Prices is either expressed by reference to an *activity schedule* (Option C) or a *bill of quantities* (Option D).

During the course of construction the *Contractor* is paid its own Defined Cost, which it has already paid out plus the Fee (referred to collectively as the Price for Work Done to Date). When the *works* are complete, the relationship between the final Price for Work Done to Date and the target price determines whether the '*Contractor's* share' is positive or negative (Figure 2.8).

In order to make this arrangement equitable to the Parties and maintain the incentive to 'out-perform' the target price, it will be necessary to adjust the target price when compensation events occur. Their effects on cost (and time) are assessed in exactly the same way under the ECC cost-based options as they are under the price-based contracts (Options A and B).

2.5.2 Disallowed Cost

The big concern for *Clients* with any cost-based contract is the risk that, in the absence of the moderating and controlling effect of agreed rates and prices for the work associated with price-based contracts, the *Contractor* will be less inclined to control costs and consequently that the *Client* will not obtain good value. It is for this reason that most cost-based contracts, the ECC included, incorporate some 'protection' for the *Client* from 'excessive' inefficiency on the part of the *Contractor*. This protection works by identifying circumstances in which certain costs will be excluded from the Defined Cost so that the *Contractor* does not get paid for them. The ECC

Figure 2.8 The *Contractor's* share

achieves this by grouping together a list of *Contractor*-controlled costs under the definition of Disallowed Cost (clause 11.2(26) for Options C, D and E, and clause 11.2(27) for Option F).

When calculating the *fee percentage* to be included with their tender submission, the *Contractor* will tend to make an assessment of the likely risk of Disallowed Cost arising, and reflect this in the *fee percentage*.

2.5.3 The *Contractor's* share (Options C and D only)

The principal difference between a target contract and a cost-reimbursable contract is that the former attempts to address the possibility of excessive inefficiency on the part of the *Contractor* by introducing the incentive of a further payment to the *Contractor* if they can complete the *works* for a cost **less** than the target price (as adjusted in accordance with the terms of the contract).

Conversely, if the final cost of the *works* exceeds the target price, it is usual with target contracts for a sum of money to be deducted from the amount due to the *Contractor*. It follows that any target contract needs to be very clear at the outset about how this further payment (to or from the *Contractor*) is to be assessed and when it becomes due.

The *Client* should be aware that some contractors, aware that their inefficiencies could result in a smaller share, could inflate the target price in the first place by tendering inflated Prices. In a competitive tender situation, this behaviour should be minimised; however, it is still a possibility.

Although simple in concept, at first sight the provisions in the ECC take some understanding, particularly clause 54.1 (clauses C54.1 and D54.5), which deals with the calculation of the 'further payment' referred to as the *Contractor's share* by the ECC. The way it works is as follows.

2.5.3.1 Deciding on the share

The *Client*, when preparing Contract Data part one, decides how they wish to 'share' with the *Contractor* any under- or over-run of the final cost against the target price. The extent of the financial risk to the Parties in the event of the final cost **exceeding** the target price can be varied between two extremes.

■ A guaranteed maximum price to the *Client* can be achieved by stating the *Contractor's share percentage* to be 100%. (In simple terms, the *Contractor* gets paid no more than the target price, and is left to absorb totally the excess over the target (referred to as the guaranteed maximum price).)

■ A minimum fee to the *Contractor* can be achieved by stating the *Contractor's share percentage* to be 0%. (In simple terms, the *Contractor* will always get paid their Defined Cost plus an additional Fee.) In essence this becomes a pure cost-reimbursable contract.

In order to understand how the *Contractor's* share is calculated under the ECC target options, an example is given below that shows a range of possible outcomes based on particular *share ranges* and *Contractor's share percentages* selected by the *Client*.

When deciding how to apportion the financial risk between the *Client* and *Contractor* by means of the share percentages, the two key factors are

■ the degree of confidence in the target price submitted
■ the incentive must be of sufficient value to produce the desired effort and economy (i.e. it should be designed to encourage savings in Defined Cost rather than encourage a temptation to exaggerate increases in the target price).

Since the idea is to provide an incentive to the *Contractor*, it may be wise not to have a high *Contractor's share percentage* for low *share ranges* or for high *share ranges*. Where, for example, the *Contractor's share percentage* is 75% for a *share range* of less than 80%, the *Contractor* could be incentivised to tender high Prices, rather than incentivised to be more efficient. It is perhaps more practical to suggest a range so that the *Contractor* is incentivised for a Price for Work Done to Date just below the total of the Prices, but less incentivised for a Price for Work Done to Date far below the total of the Prices.

An example of *share ranges* and the *Contractor's share percentage* that aims to maximise the *Contractor's* incentive is given in Table 2.3. In this example, if the Price for Work Done to Date is over 20% less than the target price (total of the Prices), then the *Contractor* is paid 20% of this under-run. They are paid less of the under-run in this instance than if the Price for Work Done to Date were between 10% and 20% less than the total of the Prices. This is based on the suggestion that if the difference is greater than 20%, the total of the Prices was incorrect, and the smaller share incentivises the *Contractor* to be more accurate about their tendered total of the Prices. Conversely, if the Price for Work Done to Date is more than 20% greater than the total of the Prices, the share of that over-run required to be paid by the *Contractor* is only 10%. This will hopefully still leave the *Contractor* with a little profit. Many *Clients* do not hold with this latter philosophy, and instead insert either 100% (as a guaranteed maximum price), or something greater than 50% as a disincentive to the *Contractor* reaching beyond the total of the Prices.

Table 2.3 Example of *share ranges* and the *Contractor's* share percentage

Share range	Contractor's share percentage
<80%	20%
80–90%	40%
90–110%	50%
110–120%	25%
>120%	10%

2.5.3.2 Paying the share The payment of the *Contractor's* share is made in two stages:

■ at Completion of the whole of the *works*, based on a forecast by the *Project Manager* at that time of the likely final out-turn cost and the likely final target price
■ later, when the actual final out-turn cost and the actual target price are agreed.

If between the above two dates the *Project Manager's* earlier forecast proves to be incorrect, the *Project Manager* has an obligation to assess the new amount due and certify a further payment.

The *share* is only calculated at Completion even though the *Contractor* could have been paid more than their *share* by the time Completion occurs (which would mean the *Contractor* having to pay back their share to the *Client*). There are two reasons why interim payments of the *Contractor's* share are not provided for before Completion of the whole of the *works*:

■ The Prices tendered by the *Contractor* (either in the form of an *activity schedule* (Option C) or a *bill of quantities* (Option D)) have the main purpose of establishing the original target price. It is not intended that their build-up should provide a realistic forecast of cash flow, and they are unlikely to be comparable with the Price for Work Done to Date (Defined Cost plus Fee) at any interim stage.

■ Forecasts of both the final Price for Work Done to Date and the final total of the Prices would be extremely uncertain at early stages of the contract. Any delays in assessing compensation events would further distort the calculation.

The danger of serious under- or over-payment of an interim *Contractor's* share has therefore led to the policy of an estimated payment on Completion, which is corrected when the assessment of the final amount due is made.

2.5.3.3 Calculation of the *Contractor's* share

Note that the following examples are for the purposes of this section only and do not form recommended ranges.

Information entered by the *Client* in Contract Data part one:

Share range	Contractor's share percentage
<90%	50%
90–120%	25%
>120%	10%

If at Completion of the whole of the *works* the *Project Manager* forecasts that the final total of the Prices (defined as the Total of the Prices in Option D) – that is, the adjusted target price – will be £10m, then the above table becomes:

Final Price for Work Done to Date[a] (share range)	Contractor's share percentage
<£9m[b]	50%
£9m to £12m[c]	25%
>£12m	10%

[a] The Price for Work Done to Date is defined in Options C and D (clause 11.2(31)).
[b] Where £9m is 90% of the forecast final total of the Prices of £10m.
[c] Where £12m is 120% of the forecast final total of the Prices of £10m.

Given the above information (the **total** of the Prices – the Total of the Prices in Option D – also known as the target price, remains the same for all these examples, at £10 million), below are examples of possible outcomes. Remember that more than one *share range* may be used per example. This is because the calculation is always taken from the middle point up or down. Where the Price for Work Done to Date is less than the total of the Prices (see examples (a) and (b) below), the calculation is made from the range within which the total of the Prices lands and continues down through all the other ranges below that. Where the Price for Work Done to Date is greater than the total of the Prices (see example (c)), the calculation is made from the range within which the total of the Prices lands and continues up through all the other ranges above that.

Example (a)   **Total/total of the Prices = £10m**

Final Price for Work Done to Date = £8m

In this example, the amount paid to the *Contractor* during the period of the contract was £8m. The total of the Prices as tendered by the *Contractor* and adjusted for compensation events was £10m. This £10m, also known as the target price, forms the base comparator for all calculations.

The final Price for Work Done to Date at £8m is less than the adjusted total of the Prices at £10m. In this instance, the calculation will breach two *share ranges* as follows. The *Contractor's share percentage* of 50% (less than £9m – see above) will be applied for the amount from £8m to £9m, the parameter for that *share range*. The *Contractor's share percentage* of 25% will be applied for the amount from £9m to £10m, which falls within the parameter of the second *share range*.

Saving under final total of the Prices	= £2m comprising two *share ranges* (where £2m = £10m total of the Prices – £8m Price for Work Done to Date)
Less than £9m	= £1m × 50% = £0.50m (£1m is the difference between £9m, which is the top of that *share range*, and £8m, the Price for Work Done to Date)
From £9m to £12m	= £1m (£1m is the difference between £9m, which is the top of the previous *share range* and £10m, which is the total of the Prices) × 25% = £0.25m
Contractor's share paid by *Client*	= £0.750m
Total amount due to the *Contractor* (excluding VAT)	= £8.75m
	This £8.75m is calculated by adding the £8m already paid to the *Contractor* to the £0.75m now due to them as the *Contractor's* share.

Example (b)   **Total/total of the Prices = £10m**

Final Price for Work Done to Date = £9.5m

In this example, the amount paid to the *Contractor* during the period of the contract was £9.50m. The total of the Prices as tendered by the *Contractor* and adjusted for compensation events was £10m. This £10m, also known as the target price, forms the base comparator for all calculations.

The final Price for Work Done to Date at £9.5m is less than the adjusted total of the Prices at £10m. In this instance, the calculation will use one *share range* only. The *Contractor's share percentage* of 25% will be applied for the amount from £9.50m to £10m, which falls within the parameter of the second *share range*.

Saving under final total of the Prices	= £0.50m comprising one *share range* (where £0.5m = £10m total of the Prices – £9.5m Price for Work Done to Date)
From £9m to £12m	= £0.50m × 25% = £0.125m (£0.5m is the difference between £10m total of the Prices within the same *share range* as the £9.5m Price for Work Done to Date)
Contractor's share paid by *Client*	= £0.125m
Total amount due to the *Contractor* (excluding VAT)	= £9.625m
	This is calculated by adding the £9.50m already paid to the *Contractor* to the £0.125m now due to them as the *Contractor's* share.

> **Example (c)**   **Total/total of the Prices = £10m**
>
> **Final Price for Work Done to Date = £11m**
>
> In this example, the amount paid to the *Contractor* during the period of the contract was £11m. The total of the Prices as tendered by the *Contractor* and adjusted for compensation events was £10m. This £10m, also known as the target price, forms the base comparator for all calculations.
>
> The final Price for Work Done to Date at £11m is more than the adjusted total of the Prices at £10m and there has been an over-run of the target price. In this instance, the calculation will use one *share range* only. The *Contractor's share percentage* of 25% will be applied for the amount from £10m to £11m, which falls within the parameter of the second *share range*.
>
> | | |
> |---|---|
> | Excess over the final total of the Prices | = £1m comprising one *share range* (where £1m = £11m Price for Work Done to Date – £10m total of the Prices) |
> | From £9m to £12m | = £1m × 25% = £0.25m (£1m is the difference between the £11m Price for Work Done to Date within the same *share range* as the £10m total of the Prices) |
> | *Contractor's* share paid to *Client* | = £0.25m |
> | Total amount due to the *Contractor* (excluding VAT) | = £10.75m |
> | | This is calculated by subtracting the amount of £0.25m now due by the *Contractor* from the £11m already paid to the *Contractor*. |

This method of calculating the *Contractor's share* is used for both Option C and D contracts.

2.5.4 Option C – target contract with *activity schedule*

An *activity schedule* (the Activity Schedule as defined in Option C) is a list of activities that is expected to be carried out by the *Contractor* in carrying out the *works*.

2.5.4.1 C1: tender

Option C requires the tenderer to tender lump sum prices against an *activity schedule* that may have been constructed by the *Client* or by the *Contractor*, depending on the instructions given by the *Client* at tender stage (see A1 in section 2.4.1.1 above). This represents the target price (total of the Prices) at which the *Contractor* estimates they can do the work described in the contract.

2.5.4.2 C2: risk

The financial risk of the project is shared by the *Contractor* and the *Client*, and target contracts therefore offer a middle-of-the-road option in terms of risk allocation. All other general and project risks are as allocated in the contract.

Option C is a popular choice of option by clients who wish to share risk. It allows a risk-and-reward approach that incentivises both Parties to work together. The cost of the *Client's* changes are visible, and the *Contractor* is incentivised to be efficient and to assist the *Client* in completing the project on time and to budget. It could also be that some *Clients* find it difficult to provide a complete Scope before the work starts, and Option C allows them to start the work sooner and for the project to continue smoothly.

2.5.4.3 C3: payment

The *Contractor* is not paid in accordance with the *activity schedule*.

During the period of the *works*, the *Contractor* is paid its Defined Cost plus its Fee (clause C11.2(31)). In other words, the *Contractor* is paid the amounts due to Subcontractors (without taking into account various amounts deducted for default) plus the amount due in accordance with the Schedule of Cost Components less Disallowed Cost plus any profit and overhead (see Chapter 2 of Book Four on the Schedule of Cost Components for a fuller explanation). It is paid its Defined Cost plus its Fee for each compensation event. The tendered Activity Schedule is not used for payment.

2.5.4.4 C4: compensation events

The Prices tendered by the *Contractor* in the *activity schedule* are used as a target price for the project (clause C11.2(32)); that is, the total of the Prices is used as the base comparator for the amount paid during the period of the contract (represented by the Price for Work Done to Date). By the nature of the payment option chosen, it is likely that the *works* will change and that compensation events will take place. The changes to the Prices quoted by the *Contractor* for implemented compensation events are used to change the Prices in the *activity schedule* (clause C63.14) so that the target price continually keeps pace with the changes to the *works*. In this way, the *activity schedule* (the target price) will keep in line with the actual job and will form a realistic target at Completion.

2.5.4.5 C5: share

At Completion (clause C54.3), the total of the Prices (i.e. the amount represented in the *activity schedule*) is compared with the Price for Work Done to Date (i.e. the total amount paid to the *Contractor*). The difference between this target price (total of the Prices) and the amount paid to the *Contractor* (Price for Work Done to Date) is shared between the *Client* and the *Contractor* in a predetermined way (as stated in Contract Data part one).

If the amount paid to the *Contractor* is greater than the target price, then the *Contractor* pays its share of the difference. If the amount paid to the *Contractor* is less than the target price, then the *Contractor* receives its share of the difference (see Section 2.5.3.3 above for an example).

2.5.4.6 C6: other considerations

There are potential difficulties with this method of payment, however.

Clients may envisage a difficulty in retrieving at Completion money that has already been paid to the *Contractor* as Price for Work Done to Date, where the Price for Work Done to Date exceeds the total of the Prices, especially if retention was not chosen as a secondary Option, or if retention does not cover the amount due.

Although retention is an obvious answer to a concern about retrieving an over-run of target cost from the *Contractor*, it does not reflect the real reason for using retention. Another way of alleviating this concern is to amend clauses to change the time when the difference between the Price for Work Done to Date and the total of the Prices is first assessed. This can be done, for example, as soon as the Price for Work Done to Date exceeds the total of the Prices, or 2 months before Completion is expected.

However, there are a number of difficulties with this approach:

- The administration of the contract has to be absolutely accurate and up to date in order to ensure that the total of the Prices fully reflects all compensation events, otherwise the basis of the comparison would be incorrect. Depending on the number of changes taking place, this might be quite difficult, particularly taking into account the passage of time in the compensation event procedure.
- The calculations taking place for every assessment date could become quite onerous, since both the Price for Work Done to Date and the total of the Prices will continue to change as time goes by. It is only when the work is complete that any difference can be assessed with any fairness, since anything can happen in contracts, and frequently does.

In general, therefore, it is recommended to rely on the contract and on the *Contractor* and to assess the risks of getting it wrong before changing the contract. Note that the definition of Price for Work Done to Date in Option C and D clause 11.2(31) includes a forecast of the *Contractor's* payments before the next assessment date.

2.5.4.7 C7: selection

A fuller discussion of the aspects to be taken into account when choosing a main Option is included in Section 2.3 above. In general, Option C should be selected when

- the scope of the work cannot be fully defined or detailed, or is uncertain

■ a reliable budget can be produced and the effects of risk can be best managed by a combined *Client* and *Contractor* team working together to meet the *Client's* objectives.

Option C can be used to form the contractual basis of a partnering approach.

Option D follows the same principle as Option C except that a *bill of quantities* is used to reach the tendered target price instead of an *activity schedule*. Usually the *bill of quantities* is drafted by the *Client*.

A fuller discussion of the aspects to be taken into account when choosing a main Option is included in Section 2.3 above. In general, Option D should be selected by the *Client* when

■ the extent of the work is not fully defined
■ a reliable budget can be produced and the effects of risk can be best managed by a combined *Client* and *Contractor* team working together to meet the *Client's* objectives
■ the *Client* or their professional team wishes to use a *bill of quantities*.

2.6. Cost-reimbursable contracts
2.6.1 Option E – cost-reimbursable contract

Option E is at the other end of risk allocation to Options A and B. In Options A and B, the *Client's* flexibility is low compared with the *Contractor's* incentive to complete on time and to budget. In Option E, the *Contractor* is paid all properly expended costs, and therefore their incentive is lower, although the *Client's* flexibility is high.

The *Contractor* is paid their Defined Cost plus their Fee during the period of the contract (clause E11.2(31)). There is no target price to compare the costs against, and therefore compensation events are of less importance from a cost perspective although they still impact the programme. Some *Clients* manage an Option E contract in the same way as Option C or D, constantly comparing the Price for Work Done to Date against an internal budget, adjusted for compensation events. This might assist the *Client* in managing their budget, but this activity is extremely onerous given that one of the reasons for choosing Option E is that the Scope is not fully developed and many compensation events are expected. Where the *Client* has their own budget that they wish to manage, some cost estimate may be required from the *Contractor*, such as the contractual requirement to provide forecasts of Defined Cost on a regular basis (clause E20.4), and compensation events may therefore acquire a renewed importance.

A fuller discussion of the aspects to be taken into account when choosing a main Option is included in Section 2.3 above. In general, Option E should be selected by the *Client* when

■ the definition of the work to be done is inadequate even for a target contract
■ an early start to construction is nevertheless required, such as safety critical, emergency repair works.

2.6.2 Option F – management contract

A management contractor contracts directly with Subcontractors and manages them on behalf of the *Client* (Figure 2.9).

ECC4 recognises that the management contractor may also undertake some works. The *Contractor* is required to indicate in Contract Data part two the work that it proposes to undertake itself.

Figure 2.9 The management contract

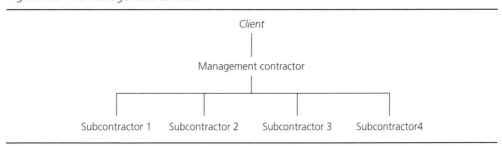

Note that Option F is not for use as a construction management contract, where the client contracts with all contractors including the construction manager who manages the works but does no part of the works themselves. In this case, it is suggested that the client contract with the construction manager using the NEC Professional Service Contract. An alternative is to purchase a licence from the publishers of the contract and amend the *conditions of contract* to reflect projects where more than one contractor is working on the site. The terms and conditions would need to reflect the greater communication and coordination required, and could also include elements such as set-off between the many contractors on the site.

A fuller discussion of the aspects to be taken into account when choosing a main Option is included in Section 2.3 of this book. In general, Option F should be selected by the *Client* when

- the *Client* sees time/cost/performance benefits from using the experience and services of a management contractor to assist in the management of a high-risk project
- the *Client* does not have the internal resources or experience to manage a project.

2.7. Administering the ECC cost-based contract

When using a cost-based contract (target price or cost-reimbursable contracts such as Options C, D, E and F), *Clients* tend to have two main doubts about their ability to control their financial commitments. The first arises from the difficulty of predicting the final cost; the second is a lack of incentive for the *Contractor* to control cost and to complete the work expeditiously.

Under a target/cost-reimbursable contract, financial control therefore takes on far greater emphasis given the increased financial risk to the *Client* under such contractual arrangements. Consequently, those main Option clauses specific to Options C, D, E and F that **do not** address how amounts due (payments) to the *Contractor* are assessed concentrate on ensuring that the *Client* (through the *Project Manager*) is afforded the opportunity for greater involvement in any matter that could impact upon the *Contractor's* Defined Cost and therefore how much the *Client* is liable to pay.

It is possible to address the lack of incentive to control cost and to complete the work expeditiously by introducing bonuses or Key Performance Indicators that reward the *Contractor* for such items as

- quality and robustness of project reporting through
  - accurately forecasting the final out-turn cost of the project
  - audit of Defined Cost
  - programme/time management
- bonuses for early completion.

2.7.1 Greater financial control by the *Client*

This section addresses how the ECC provides for the *Client* to exercise greater control over matters that could impact upon Defined Cost.

2.7.1.1 Clause 20.3

Clause 20.3 (for main Options C, D, E and F) states that the *Contractor* advises the *Project Manager* on the practical implications of the *Client's* design of the *works* and on subcontracting arrangements. Although such obligations are typical for cost-based contracts and reflective of the assumed closer degree of co-operation and openness between the Parties, there is little guidance given as to how detailed the advice should be and no contractual sanctions applied to the *Contractor* who fails to enter into the spirit of the provision.

Value management including value engineering provisions are part of the ECC through clause 16 and main Option clauses A63.12, B63.12, C63.13 and D63.13, and could be used, for example, to allow the *Contractor* to identify a design they believe to be more economic and practical to construct. The effect of such a provision, if more economic designs proposed by the *Contractor* are adopted, is that both the *Client* and the *Contractor* benefit financially in proportion to any share mechanism included. This is a provision designed to encourage the *Contractor* to maximise their share potential (profit), while at the same time reducing the overall cost to the *Client*.

2.7.1.2 Clause 20.4

Clause 20.4 (for main Options C, D, E and F) emphasises the need for the *Client*, through the *Project Manager*, to be more financially aware under cost-based contractual arrangements. It states that

> 'The *Contractor* prepares forecasts of the total Defined Cost for the whole of the *works* in consultation with the *Project Manager* and submits them to the *Project Manager*. Forecasts are prepared at the intervals stated in the Contract Data from the *starting date* until Completion of the whole of the *works*. An explanation of the changes made since the previous forecast is submitted with each forecast.'

Although there is no clear contractual purpose for the forecasts, if prepared carefully they are vitally important to financial awareness and cost control, since they will identify any deviations from the *Contractor's* financial assumptions included with the original tender. To maximise the benefit of these forecasts it is recommended that the following steps are taken:

1 Request tenderers in their tender submission to give a full breakdown of their tender price, showing all their assumptions regarding resource levels, outputs, input costs, subcontracting arrangements and risk allowances. This information is essential for two purposes: first, it allows the *Client*, as part of the tender assessment, to determine whether the tender submitted is realistic: second, and more relevant to cost forecasting, it effectively provides the first forecast of the total Defined Cost for the whole of the *works*, and is therefore the yardstick for all subsequent forecasts.
2 Include in the Scope a description of the minimum level of detail and the format required for the forecasts. This is important because the ECC requirement for forecasts is very broad in terms of the detail required and, if no further guidance were to be provided in the Scope, forecasts that serve no useful purpose may result. All of these forecasts essentially have two components:
   – the costs committed in providing the *works* that have been completed up to the date that the forecast is prepared
   – the current estimate to complete the remaining *works*.

When preparing the Scope, it should be ensured that these forecasts yield reliable information that can be used to identify problem areas requiring investigations, but at the same time utilising as far as possible any existing cost monitoring/control systems the *Contractor* has in place. More sophisticated techniques such as earned value analysis can be used to assist in the preparation of the forecasts, but the golden rule must be to keep the forecasts as simple as possible consistent with providing reliable information. Any forecast of the total Defined Cost of the whole of the *works* will only be as reliable as the accuracy of the following elements of it:

■ the measurement at the forecast date of the physical work done
■ the accuracy of the overall costs committed in completing the work done and, just as important, the overall **allocation** of those costs to the appropriate activities
■ the accuracy of the estimate of costs for the work remaining to be done at the forecast date.

If all this sounds like hard work, it is worth remembering that the success or failure of a contract is closely related to the managerial effort expended by the Parties administering the contract.

Construction planning is largely concerned with the efficient use of labour and constructional plant. In any type of cost-based contract the *Client* pays for most or all of these resources on an actual cost basis. Since the cost of such resources is mainly time-related, the *Client* should concern themselves with this aspect of contract management. There is consequently a strong case on cost-based contracts for a joint cost and planning team comprising personnel from the *Contractor's* and the *Project Manager's* team working from the same offices producing revised programmes (as required by clause 32.2), forecasts of the total Defined Cost for the whole of the *works* (clause 20.4) and quotations in respect of any compensation events that arise (as required by clause 62.2).

Forecasts are prepared at intervals stated in the Contract Data. Many contractors only prepare such forecasts internally on a 3-month basis. The greater financial risk accrued by the *Client* on a cost-based contract justifies such forecasts being prepared on a more frequent basis.

2.7.1.3 Subcontracts

It was stated above that Defined Cost as defined includes payments that the *Contractor* makes to Subcontractors in accordance with the terms of the latter's subcontract. It follows therefore that the *Project Manager* should have a greater awareness of the commercial details of subcontracts, and may wish to include in the Scope the procurement procedures to be followed by the *Contractor* for all subcontracted work (over, say, a stipulated value), and likewise for supply contracts. The safeguards provided by the ECC in respect of work that the *Contractor* elects to subcontract are as follows:

- Before appointing a proposed Subcontractor the *Contractor* must submit the name to the *Project Manager* for acceptance. The *Contractor* is not permitted to appoint a proposed Subcontractor until the *Project Manager* has accepted them (clause 26.2), and doing so is grounds for termination (clause 91.2 (R13)).
- Before appointing a proposed Subcontractor the *Contractor* must submit the proposed subcontract documents to the *Project Manager* for acceptance (clause 26.3), unless either a contract in the NEC suite of documents is to be used unamended other than in accordance with the *additional conditions of contract* (i.e. the subcontract may be amended in the same way as any Z clauses in the main contract) or the *Project Manager* has agreed that no submission is required.
- Specific to the cost-based Options of the ECC (C, D, E and F), clause 26.4 requires the *Contractor* to submit the pricing information in the proposed subcontract documents for each subcontractor to the *Project Manager* for acceptance, unless the *Project Manager* has agreed that no submission is required.

Given the all-too-common occurrence of a failure by contractors to understand the Schedule of Cost Components and its related commercial percentages, it is the pricing information that probably represents the greatest likelihood of the *Client* paying 'over the odds' on a cost-based contract.

In summary, subcontracted work represents a specific risk to the *Client* under an ECC cost-based contract, and it is recommended that careful consideration is given to the inclusion in the Scope of procurement procedures that ensure the *Project Manager* is kept advised throughout.

2.7.2 Assessing and verifying the *Contractor's* Defined Cost

This section addresses how, under the ECC, amounts due to the *Contractor* are assessed and, given the cost-based nature of these sums, how the *Client* verifies that such costs have been properly incurred by the *Contractor*.

In any cost-based contract, both Parties are primarily concerned with Defined Cost – that is, that cost as defined (clauses C11.2(24), D11.2(24), E11.2(24) and F11.2(25)) and incurred by the *Contractor* in carrying out the work. Consequently, it is essential that the *Project Manager* starts to think in terms of cost and the manner in which construction costs are incurred rather than the unit price approach more commonplace with the majority of price-based contracts. The *Contractor's* accounts and records for the contract must be open to scrutiny by the *Project Manager*, who will need to establish monitoring and auditing procedures to ensure that these documents and records constitute an accurate reflection of the costs properly incurred by the *Contractor* in providing the *works* defined in the contract. Inspection should proceed and be completed concurrently with the construction work.

There is no express mention of 'inspections' by the *Project Manager* in the ECC. Instead, and sensibly, the ECC merely describes in general terms the accounts and records that the *Contractor* is obliged to keep (clauses C52.2, D52.2, E52.2 and F52.3), and that it must give the *Project Manager* the facility to inspect its accounts and records (clause 52.4). It is for the *Project Manager* to determine the nature and frequency of their 'inspections' of the *Contractor's* accounts and records, with the objective of providing confidence to the *Client* that the latter is only being required to pay those amounts to which the *Contractor* is entitled in accordance with the terms and conditions of the contract.

Consistent with providing the necessary 'confidence', inspections should be designed to achieve maximum 'value' from minimum effort. They should be structured and focused, recognising that in some cases 80% of the *Contractor's* total Defined Cost will be represented by 20% of the cost components listed in the Schedule of Cost Components. They should concentrate on the 'higher-risk' cost components such as subcontracted work, internal plant hire and 'muck-away'. They should be carried out concurrent with the construction work so that their findings are able to support as closely as practicable the assessment by the *Project Manager* of amounts due to the *Contractor*. An example inspection plan is included in Appendix 3 below. Exhaustive inspections are not always necessary; random inspections may suffice.

> On a major infrastructure project, a detailed inspection plan was prepared by the project team for the tunnels and stations contract, which left the *Contractor* in no doubt as to the nature and frequency of the inspections to be carried out by the *Project Manager* and the information, in the form of accounts and records, that they were expected to provide. Despite some initial resistance, once the inspections were under way the *Contractor* admitted that some of the inspection findings were beneficial in identifying where it was necessary to 'tighten up' their internal procedures.

Below is an example of the detailed checks that should form part of any inspection of the *Contractor's* costs under an ECC cost-based contract. To practitioners more familiar with the unit pricing more common with price-based contracts, the auditing of a *Contractor's* costs can seem rather daunting. It is therefore useful to remember that on any construction contract all of the *Contractor's* costs fall into one of the following categories:

- direct costs of production
- indirect costs of production (site overheads/on-costs)
- risk allowances not included above
- head office overheads
- profit.

In turn, each of these (with the exception of the last two) constitutes the cost of one or more of the following components:

- people (labour and staff)
- construction plant
- materials
- Subcontractors
- miscellaneous other charges (e.g. rents payable for temporary occupation of land).

It should not be surprising then that the Schedule of Cost Components, which is the list of admissible costs constituting Defined Cost for **non-subcontracted works**, is broken down into similar cost headings, namely

- people
- Equipment (construction plant and other temporary works)
- Plant and Materials (things incorporated into the permanent works)
- Subcontractors
- charges
- manufacture and fabrication outside the Working Areas
- design done outside the Working Areas
- insurances.

The inspection when carried out is seeking to ensure the following:

- Only Defined Cost as defined by reference to the Schedule of Cost Components is included in amounts due to the *Contractor*.
- Cost components not listed in the Schedule of Cost Components are not included in the calculation of Defined Cost. Given that all of the *Contractor's* costs, which are not listed

in the Schedule of Cost Components, are deemed to be covered by the Fee (clause 52.1), if such costs are also taken into Defined Cost there will effectively be a 'double' payment.

■ Any Disallowed Cost as defined (main Options C, D, E clause 11.2(26), and Option F clause 11.2(27)) is identified.

2.7.3 Payment procedures

The principal component of amounts due (payments) to the *Contractor* under the ECC is the Price for Work Done to Date, defined (clause 11.2(31) of Options C, D, E and F) as 'the total Defined Cost which the *Project Manager* forecasts will have been paid by the *Contractor* before the next assessment date plus the Fee'. Expanding this definition, the amount due to the *Contractor* comprises

■ amounts paid by the *Contractor* in respect of any of the components listed in the Schedule of Cost Components, less any Disallowed Cost

■ the Fee calculated by applying the *fee percentage* to the first bullet above.

The important point to draw from the above definition is that interim amounts certified to the *Contractor* include amounts that the *Project Manager* forecasts will have been **paid (not incurred)** by the *Contractor* up to the date that the *Project Manager* next assesses the amount due. Consequently, costs committed by the *Contractor* and invoices received but forecast to be not yet paid at the next assessment date are excluded.

2.8. Dispute resolution procedure Options

In the ECC, dispute resolution procedure Options are contained in Options W1, W2 and W3.

■ Option W1 is to be used where adjudication is the preferred route of dispute resolution but the HGCR Act does not apply; that is, in countries other than the UK, and in the UK where the contract is not a construction contract as defined in the Act.

■ Option W2 is to be used in the UK where the HGCR Act applies to the contract. Note that the Local Democracy, Economic Development and Construction Act 2009 amends some parts of the HGCR Act, and the ECC has been amended accordingly.

■ Option W3 is to be used where the Parties to a contract want to refer a disputed matter in the first instance to a Dispute Avoidance Board, whose task is to keep up to date with the progress of the project and to seek to avoid disputes before they happen.

Chapter 4 of Book Three discusses dispute resolution in detail. A brief description of Options W1, W2 and W3 is included below.

2.8.1 Option W1

Option W1 is to be used when the HGCR Act does not apply. The dispute resolution procedure has three levels as follows:

1 Both the *Client* and the *Contractor* name *Senior Representatives* in their Contract Data, and a dispute is referred to the *Senior Representatives* as a first level of dispute resolution.

2 Where a Party is dissatisfied with the outcome of the first level of dispute resolution, it may refer a dispute to an *Adjudicator*, named in Contract Data part one by the *Client*, who then considers the dispute and makes a decision in accordance with the NEC Dispute Resolution Service Contract.

3 Where a Party is dissatisfied with the outcome of the adjudication, they may refer the dispute to the *tribunal* (usually litigation or arbitration) as the final level of dispute resolution.

Option W1 describes the following:

■ A dispute is referred to the *Senior Representatives* in the first instance.

■ The Parties identify *Senior Representatives* in the Contract Data.

■ Disputes are referred in accordance with the Dispute Reference Table in clause W1.1.

■ The Parties appoint the *Adjudicator* under the NEC Dispute Resolution Service Contract at the *starting date* (clause W1.2(1)). It is unlikely that most Parties will undertake this task; they are more likely to include in the Contract Data an adjudicator nominating body to name an *Adjudicator* for appointment when the need arises (i.e. when the Parties fall into dispute and adjudication is required).

- An *Adjudicator nominating body* (identified in the Contract Data) can choose an adjudicator if the originally chosen one is not identified in the Contract Data, or if the chosen *Adjudicator* resigns or is unable to act (clause W1.2(3)).
- The type of *tribunal* is included in the Contract Data and, if the *tribunal* is arbitration, the *arbitration procedure* to be followed and the place where the arbitration is to take place are also included in the Contract Data.

The rest of Option W1 describes the procedures to be followed when a dispute has been referred, and includes the procedures for referring a dispute to the *tribunal*.

2.8.2 Option W2

Dispute resolution procedure Option W2 is to be used only in the UK when the HGCR Act applies to the contract. The Option prescribes the procedure for statutory adjudication, as dictated by the HGCR Act, and describes three levels of disputes resolution as follows:

1 Both the *Client* and the *Contractor* name *Senior Representatives* in their Contract Data, and a dispute is referred to the *Senior Representatives* as a first level of dispute resolution.
2 Where a Party is dissatisfied with the outcome of the first level of dispute resolution, it may refer a dispute to an *Adjudicator*, named in Contract Data part one by the *Client*, who then considers the dispute and makes a decision in accordance with the NEC Dispute Resolution Service Contract. However, a Party may also refer a dispute to the *Adjudicator* at any time, and a Party is not required to first refer a dispute to the *Senior Representatives*, but it is likely that this route will be encouraged by the *Client* as a potentially quicker and more cost-effective resolution than adjudication.
3 Where a Party is dissatisfied with the outcome of the adjudication, they may refer the dispute to the *tribunal* (usually litigation or arbitration) as the final level of dispute resolution.

The assumption made within Option W1 with regard to appointing the *Adjudicator* under the NEC4 Dispute Resolution Service Contract at the *starting date* is also made in Option W2 (clause W2.2(3)). It is unlikely that most Parties will undertake this task; they are more likely to include in the Contract Data an adjudicator nominating body to name an *Adjudicator* for appointment when the need arises (i.e. when the Parties fall into dispute and adjudication is required), and Option W2 does allow for an *Adjudicator nominating body* (identified in the Contract Data) to choose an adjudicator if the originally chosen one is not identified in the Contract Data, or if they resign or are unable to act (clause W2.2(5)).

The most important aspect of Option W2 to highlight is that a Party may refer a dispute to the *Adjudicator* at any time (clause W2.2(1)). This is required by the HGCR Act, and it is onerous for the *Client*.

The rest of Option W2 details the procedures required to be followed in the event of an adjudication under this Option.

2.8.3 Option W3

There are only two levels of dispute resolution in Option W3, which makes use of a Dispute Avoidance Board, the members of which are included in the Contract Data parts one and two. The Dispute Avoidance Board is appointed under the NEC Dispute Resolution Service Contract current at the *starting date*.

A dispute is referred to the Dispute Avoidance Board that

- visits the Site at intervals dictated by Contract Data part one
- inspects the progress of the *works* and become aware of any potential differences
- can review all potential disputes and help the Parties to settle them without the need for the dispute to be formally referred
- provides a recommendation for resolving the difference.

A dissatisfied Party can then refer the matter to the *tribunal*.

2.9. Secondary Options
2.9.1 Selection of the secondary Option

The main Option chosen by the *Client*, together with the chosen secondary Options and the resolving and avoiding disputes options, describe the contract strategy for the particular project required. With the few exceptions that are outlined in the schedule of Options on page 1 of the ECC, the *Client* may choose any, all or none of the secondary Options. The exceptions are as follows: Option X1 may not be used with Options E and F; Option X3 may not be chosen with Options C, D, E and F; Option X16 may not be used with Option F; Option X20 may not be used with Option X12; and Option X22 may not be used with Options A, B, D and F.

One of the principles behind this pick-and-mix approach is that some of the secondary Options may increase the cost of the project. In some traditional contracts, for example, retention and a performance bond are written into the standard conditions of contract, whether the *Client* requires these aspects of the contract or not. The *Client* therefore pays for these aspects even if they do not want them.

The flexible approach of the ECC towards contract elements such as liquidated damages, retention and performance bonds means that the *Client* has a choice about what aspects of the contract are important to them, and what they are prepared to pay for.

2.9.1.1 Option X1 – price adjustment for inflation (only used with Options A, B, C and D)

The addition of a price fluctuation clause to main Options E and F is unnecessary, as it is a fully cost-reimbursable contract. Under main Options A to D, all change is valued at Defined Cost, therefore automatically allowing for any and all price fluctuations. However, Option X1 requires the adjustment of compensation event assessments to return to base date levels. Consequently, the Price Adjustment Factor is applied to the whole amount due at each assessment date.

When Option X1 is included, adjustments are made in accordance with the additional defined terms for which values are required in Contract Data part one as follows:

- the Base Date Index (B) is the latest available index before the *base date*
- the Latest Index (L) is the latest available index before the date of assessment of an amount due
- the Price Adjustment Factor is the total of the products of each of the proportions stated in the Contract Data multiplied by $(L - B)/B$ for the index linked to it.

The total of the Prices for the contract are divided into a series of proportions, for example

- substructure
- superstructure
- building services
- external works.

Each is linked to an index published by a source – also identified and containing the price fluctuations for the appropriate element of work. Provision is made in the Contract Data to identify a proportion of the *works*, which remains non-adjustable.

Option X1 goes on to define the administration of the Price Adjustment Factor separately for Options A and B and Options C and D.

2.9.1.2 Option X2 – changes in the law

The inclusion of Option X2 makes a change in the *law of the contract* a compensation event if it occurs after the Contract Date. The *Client* carries the risk of all resultant cost and time effects.

In the absence of this secondary Option, under general law the time effects of changes in the law are at the *Contractor's* risk, and so this Option would generally be used for longer-term contracts where changes in the law may be unpredictable.

2.9.1.3 Option X3 – multiple currencies (used only with Options A and B)

Two identified terms are fundamental to this Option for which the *Client* in Contract Data part one enters values as

- *currency of the contract*
- *exchange rates.*

Contract Data part one will also contain a list of the items and activities that will be paid in a currency other than the *currency of the contract*, along with the currency and the maximum amount to be paid in that currency. Amounts above the maximum amount for a listed activity will be paid in the *currency of the contract*.

Also relevant to Option X3 are the contents of clause 51.1, which states that all payments are in the *currency of the contract* unless otherwise stated in this contract. The cost-reimbursable main Options C and D clause 50.7 and Options E and F clause 50.8 state that payments of Defined Cost made by the *Contractor* in another currency are to be paid to them by the *Client* in the same currency. For calculation of the Fee and any *Contractor's* share, the payments are converted to the *currency of the contract*.

2.9.1.4 Option X4 – the ultimate holding company guarantee

Rather than referring to a parent company guarantee, Option X4 requires that the *Contractor* provides

■ a guarantee of the *Contractor's* performance from the ultimate holding company (i.e. where the *Contractor* is a subsidiary of another company, the guarantee must come from the parent of that other company, or perhaps even *its* ultimate holding company) or
■ a proposal for an alternative guarantor that is also owned by the ultimate holding company.

The form for the guarantee must be set out in the Scope.

2.9.1.5 Option X5 – sectional completion

Sectional completion provides for the *Client* to take over *sections* of the *works* as they are completed.

This Option operates by redefining all references in the contract conditions to the *works*, Completion and the Completion Date. These terms subsequently apply to either the whole of the *works* or any *section* of the *works* as is relevant to the context. Note that the *defects date* still runs from Completion of the whole of the *works*.

Through Option X5, separate Completion Dates are set for the *sections* of the *works* stated in Contract Data part one. Additionally, Contract Data part one allows for sectional Completion Dates to be related to bonuses under Option X6 and delay damages under Option X7.

2.9.1.6 Option X6 – bonus for early completion

This Option puts in place a bonus to be paid to the *Contractor* for completing the *works* earlier than the Completion Date (with Options C, D and E, the *Contractor* could expend more – and the *Client* pay more – in order to earn the bonus).

The amount per day is stated in Contract Data part one, and is multiplied by the number of days from earlier Completion (or the date on which the *Client* takes over the *works* – whichever is the earlier) until the Completion Date shown on the latest Accepted Programme.

When Options X6 and X5 (sectional completion) are used together, an amount per day for each section of the *works* is stated.

> A contract to build a large casino in an entertainment complex included a bonus for early Completion of £40 000 per day. The owner of the casino knew that he could make at least £40 000 per day every day that the casino was open.

2.9.1.7 Option X7 – delay damages

This option contains the converse provision to Option X6 in that the *Contractor* pays delay damages at the amount per day for each day that Completion (or the date on which the *Client* takes over the *works*) is later than the Completion Date as shown on the latest Accepted Programme.

The delay damages used through Option X7 are liquidated damages, the purpose of which is twofold:

- to provide compensation to the *Client*
- to limit the liability of the *Contractor* for failing to complete the *works* by the required date.

Through legal precedent, liquidated damages must be a genuine pre-estimate of the *Client's* loss or a lesser sum. The inclusion of a greater amount in Contract Data part one as a penalty will render the provisions of Option X7 unenforceable under law. The *Client* must be able to demonstrate, if required, that the calculations were done before the start of the contract and that they estimated the *Client's* losses in the event that the *Contractor* completed later than required.

In the absence of Option X7, the *Client* is entitled by law to pursue the *Contractor* for damages at large. It is important to remember that this right is removed by including Option X7, and the *Client* becomes entitled only to the amount per day stated in the Contract Data. Careful consideration must be given to the value entered.

Again as with Option X6, Option X7 can be used in conjunction with Option X5 (sectional completion), and separate amounts per day for delay damages can be stated in the Contract Data for each *section* of the *works*.

Clause X7.3 describes the procedure to reduce delay damages in the situation where the *Client* takes over a part of the *works* before Completion. The delay damages are reduced immediately from the date of take over of the part of the *works*, and the delay damages are reduced by the same proportion assessed by the *Project Manager* as the benefit to the *Client* of taking over that part of the *works* rather than all the *works* not previously taken over.

2.9.1.8 Option X8 – undertakings to the *Client* and Others	The *Client* enters in Contract Data part one

- *undertakings to Others* that are the *Contractor's* responsibility to deliver
- *Subcontractor undertaking to Others* and *Subcontractor undertaking to the Client* that the *Contractor* arranges the Subcontractor to provide.

The undertakings are in the form stated in the Scope. This Option may be used for collateral warranties.

2.9.1.9 Option X9 – transfer of rights	Most clients prefer to own the design prepared as part of the contract, and Option X9 facilitates this ownership. Any part of the design that the *Client* does not want to own or that they cannot own is stated in the Scope.

2.9.1.10 Option X10 – information modelling	Where the *Client* wishes to use building information modelling, Option X10 facilitates the extra collaboration required, as well as an extra early warning and compensation event and extra liabilities. The Option refers to an Information Execution Plan in the Contract Data, and allows the *Client* to receive the first plan either with the tender or after the start of the contract.

2.9.1.11 Option X11 – termination by the *Client*	The *Client* may terminate the *Contractor's* obligations to Provide the Works for a reason not identified in the Termination Table by notifying the *Project Manager* and *Contractor*. The Option also lists the termination procedures to be used and the amount due on termination.

2.9.1.12 Option X12 – multiparty collaboration (not used with Option X20)	Option X12 is broken into a number of key components as follows:

- identified and defined terms (clauses X12(1) to X12(7)) – defines the Partners, the Own Contract, the Core Group, Partnering Information and Key Performance Indicators
- actions (clause X12.2) – spells out what actions the Partners will take
- collaboration (clause X12.3) – specifies how the Partners will work together
- incentives (clause X12.4) – sets out how much a Partner is paid and what additional payments they may receive for meeting any Key Performance Indicators.

There is no definition/identification of the *Client's* representative, who leads the Core Group unless otherwise stated in the Partnering Information. Presumably it is the *Project Manager*;

however, it could be any member of the *Client* organisation who can be construed as representing the *Client*.

2.9.1.13 Option X13 – the performance bond

Like many other options, bonds cost the *Contractor* money that they are likely to pass on to the *Client*. The reasoning for choosing such options should be carefully considered (for more information, see Chapter 3 below on completing the Contract Data).

Options X13 and X4 (ultimate holding company guarantee) should not be chosen together but as alternatives. These Options require the *Contractor* to complete bonds and parent company guarantees in the form stated in the Scope. This provides the flexibility for the individual project to specify a form of bond or guarantee appropriate to their individual needs. The amount for a performance bond is stated in the Contract Data part one by the *Client*.

If the bond is considered important, then the following additions could be made to the contract:

- It could be stated in the conditions of tendering that the bond is required before execution of the contract.
- An Option Z clause could be added to ensure that the bond is received, for example: 'One quarter of the Price for Work Done to Date is retained in assessments of the amount due until the *Contractor* has submitted the performance bond required under Option X13 to the *Project Manager* for acceptance.'

2.9.1.14 Option X14 – advanced payment to the *Contractor*

Where the *Contractor* is required to make a large capital investment such as marble tiling or the procurement of plant and machinery or special equipment, and needs financial support in order to procure the materials at the beginning of the contract, the *Client* could choose to lend the *Contractor* this money as an advanced payment. Another way of achieving this type of payment is through the *activity schedule* (through adding an activity in the *activity schedule* (Option A) for the purchase of the material so that the *Contractor* is paid on completion of that activity) or the *bill of quantities* (through adding an item in the *bill of quantities* that can be assessed at the assessment date).

The information required in the Contract Data for operation of this Option is as follows:

- the amount of advanced payment
- the period after which repayment instalments begin
- the amount of instalments
- the requirement for advanced payment bond.

Where such an advanced payment is made, the amount is stated in Contract Data part one, and the amount is included in the first assessment of the amount due or (if an advanced payment bond is required) in the next assessment after the *Client* receives the advanced payment bond.

The *Client* may choose whether they want an advanced payment bond or not. A bank or insurer that has been accepted by the *Project Manager* issues an advanced payment bond. The *Project Manager* may reject the proposed bondsman if its commercial position is not strong enough. The Scope stipulates the form of the bond, and Contract Data part one stipulates the amount of the instalments that the *Contractor* pays the *Client* in each amount due following the period stated in Contract Data part one. The bond is for the amount of the advanced payment that the *Contractor* has not repaid.

2.9.1.15 Option X15 – the *Contractor's* design

In the absence of this secondary Option, the *Contractor's* liability for Defects in the *works* due to their design is 'fitness for purpose'. In simple terms, this means that the finished *works* must fulfil the function for which they were intended.

The inclusion of Option X15 in the contract conditions limits the standard of liability to using the skill and care normally used by professionals designing works similar to the *works*, bringing it in line with the liability placed on professional designers. This is particularly useful in design-

and-build contracts, where the contractor may be unable to purchase fitness-for-purpose insurance for their design.

It is important to remember several key points.

- The limitation applies to Defects arising as a result of the *Contractor's* design and not to the design itself.
- The *Contractor's* compliance with 'fitness-for-purpose' or 'reasonable skill and care' can only be determined by reference to the *Client's* requirements as stated in the Scope.
- Through section 4 of the core clauses, the *Contractor* is required to correct Defects before the end of the *defect correction period*, which commences at Completion for Defects notified before Completion and when the Defect is notified for other Defects. The liabilities placed on the *Contractor* by secondary Option X15 cannot therefore be acted upon by the *Client* until after Completion of the *works*.

Clause X15.2 makes it clear that the *Contractor's* correction of a Defect for which they are not liable under this contract is a compensation event.

2.9.1.16 Option X16 – retention (not used with Option F)

Retention is a fundamental issue that has traditionally formed a part of the main body of clauses in most conventional contracts. The reasons for requesting retention should be carefully considered, since it costs the *Contractor* to forego a part of the money due to them every month. This reminds the *Client* of the need for a careful review of the secondary Options to ensure that the desired provisions form part of the contract document.

Retention with Option X16 allocates a *retention-free amount*, where for an identified period at the beginning of the project the *Client* will not withhold an amount from the *Contractor*, smoothing the *Contractor's* cash flow when they need it most. If the *Client* wishes to use retention in the traditional manner, they may enter an amount of nil as the *retention-free amount*. It follows that if the *retention-free amount* is an amount equal to 50% of the total of the Prices at the Contract Date, then retention would be taken at double the usual amount to accumulate to the same amount at Completion.

An example is given in Figure 2.10.

Two items of information must be included in the Contract Data to operate Option X16:

- the *retention-free amount* (intended to assist the *Contractor's* cash flow during the early stages of the contract)
- the *retention percentage* (applied to all amounts due in excess of the above).

Figure 2.10 Retention

  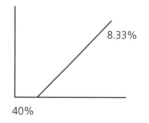

A *retention-free amount* of 0% of the total of the Prices at the Contract Date means that retention will be deducted from the first assessment of the amount due and that the *retention percentage* can be a typical 5%.	A *retention-free amount* of 50% of the total of the Prices at the Contract Date means that retention will start to be deducted once the value of the *works* are approximately 50% complete. This means that the *retention percentage* should be increased to 10% to arrive at the same retention amount at Completion.	A *retention-free amount* of 40% of the total of the Prices at the Contract Date means that retention will start to be deducted once the value of the *works* are approximately 40% complete. This means that the *retention percentage* should be increased to 8.33% to arrive at the same retention amount at Completion.

On amounts due, the *Client* retains the *retention percentage* applied to the Price for Work Done to Date exceeding the *retention-free amount* until the earlier of the Completion of the whole of the *works* or the date on which the *Client* takes over the whole of the *works*. This amount is halved at that point, and the remainder is paid to the *Contractor* following issue of the Defects Certificate.

2.9.1.17 Option X17 – low-performance damages

This Option states that where a Defect included in the Defects Certificate shows low performance with respect to a performance level stated in the Contract Data, the *Contractor* pays the amount of low-performance damages stated in the Contract Data.

In order to ensure that this option operates effectively where invoked, the *Client* must ensure the Defect is measurable against information in both the Scope and the Contract Data. These types of requirements are usual with process plant (e.g. water treatment, power stations and factories).

> If, for example, the Defect is in relation to the electrical consumption of a heating system, the performance specification in the Scope must be clear and provide all necessary values such as the heating levels to be achieved against the acceptable levels of electricity use. The statements given in the Contract Data regarding the amount of damages and the corresponding performance level must be linked to the Scope in a way that allows the identification of 'low performance'.

2.9.1.18 Option X18 – limitation of liability

There are five Contract Data entries required in Contract Data part one. Because the inclusion of the clauses and associated Contract Data part one statements restrict liability to the degree stated, it may be read into the contract that their exclusion results in liability being unlimited.

Clause X18.1 restricts the *Contractor's* liability to the *Client* for the *Client's* indirect or consequential loss. The amount of the restriction is stated in the Contract Data: 'The *Contractor's* liability to the *Client* for indirect or consequential loss is limited to …'.

It should be noted that there is no limit for direct losses unless a cap on the total liability is stated in clause X18.4.

Clause X18.2 restricts the *Contractor's* liability to the *Client* for loss of or damage to the *Client's* property. The amount of the restriction is stated in the Contract Data: 'For any one event, the *Contractor's* liability to the *Client* for loss of or damage to the *Client's* property is limited to …'.

One should note the phrase 'for any one event'; the sum stated here is therefore not a total liability but a total liability for any one event. These words are consistent with the wording usually found in insurance policies for *Client's* property.

Clause X18.3 restricts the *Contractor's* liability to the *Client* for Defects due to their design that are not listed on the Defects Certificate. The amount of the restriction is stated in the Contract Data: 'The *Contractor's* liability for Defects due to its design which are not listed on the Defects Certificate is limited to …'. There is no reason why the Contract Data sentence could not read 'The *Contractor's* liability for Defects due to its design that are not listed on the Defects Certificate is unlimited.' This clause covers what are effectively latent Defects.

Clause X18.4 restricts the *Contractor's* total liability to the *Client* except for the excluded matters listed in the clause. The excluded matters are amounts payable by the *Contractor*, such as

- loss or damage to the *Client's* property
- delay damages if Option X7 applies
- low-performance damages if Option X17 applies
- *Contractor's* share if Option C or D applies.

Some *Clients* include in the list of excluded matters such additional items as

- death or personal injury to any person
- wilful default, fraud or abandonment by the *Contractor*.

The amount of the restriction is stated in the Contract Data: 'The *Contractor's* total liability to the *Client* for all matters arising under or in connection with this contract, other than the excluded matters, is limited to …'. If a *Client* does not include this clause in the Contract Data, there is a possibility that a *Contractor* may request that it is included. It is possible that an interpretation of its absence by choice could be that the liability is unlimited.

Clause X18.5 restricts the *Contractor's* liability to the *Client* to a specific period of time after the Completion of the whole of the *works*. The statement in Contract Data part one reads, 'The *end of liability date* is … years after Completion of the whole of the *works*.' Once again, *Contractors* may require this clause to be included in their contracts.

A *Client* may not wish to incorporate all five limitations into their contract. In such a situation, it is suggested that only the relevant clauses are included in the Contract Data. For example, in the list of Options in the first entry in Contract Data part one, a *Client* could include 'A, X7, X18.2, X18.3, Y(UK)2 and Z'.

2.9.1.19 Option X20 – Key Performance Indicators (not used with Option X12)

Option X20 is for use in contracts where the partnering Option X12 is not used, as Key Performance Indicators are already included in Option X12. This Option reflects the trend towards the inclusion of Key Performance Indicators in contracts, and rewards *Contractors* for achieving an aspect of performance (health and safety, time, programme, etc.).

Clause X20.1 requires an Incentive Schedule to be produced that identifies aspects of performance for which the *Contractor* is to be incentivised. The *Contractor* is required by clause X20.2 to report to the *Project Manager* their performance and forecast of final measurement against each Key Performance Indicator at the intervals stated in the Contract Data, from the *starting date* until the Defects Certificate.

If at the performance assessment interval the *Contractor* is not on target to achieve the target set in the Incentive Schedule, they submit to the *Project Manager* their proposals for improving performance (clause X20.3). Note that there is no disincentive for not achieving the target Key Performance Indicators.

The *Contractor* is paid (clause X20.4) the amount stated in the Incentive Schedule if the target stated is achieved or improved upon. Payment of the amount due is when the target has been improved upon or achieved.

Clause X20.5 allows the *Client* to add a Key Performance Indicator and associated payment to the Incentive Schedule. They are not allowed to delete or reduce a payment stated in the Incentive Schedule.

The layout for the Incentive Schedule will be similar to that contained in the partnering Option X12.

2.9.1.20 Option X21 – whole-life cost

This clause enables the *Contractor* to propose a change to the Scope that reduces the operating and maintenance cost of an asset. If the *Project Manager* is prepared to consider the change, the *Contractor* provides a quotation. The *Project Manager* consults with the *Contractor* about the quotation, and either accepts or does not accept the proposal. If the *Project Manager* accepts the proposal, then they change the Scope, the Prices, the Completion Date and the Key Dates accordingly and accept the revised programme.

Option X21 encourages both Parties to look beyond the price of the *works* and to consider the operating and maintenance costs of the *works*, as *Clients* too often only realise after the *defects date* that the cost of operating and maintaining a property is significantly more than anticipated because they had only evaluated the price of the *works* and not the whole-life cost of the asset.

2.9.1.21 Option X22 – early *Contractor* involvement (used only with options C and E)

Option X22 facilitates early engagement with the *Contractor*. Options C and E both provide opportunities for the *Contractor* and the *Client* to work closer together, and Option X22 uses this ethos and builds on it. The procedure involves the following:

- The *Client* discloses the Budget in Contract Data part one, with details included in the Scope; and the Budget can be changed following discussions between the *Project Manager* and the *Contractor*.
- The *Contractor* provides pricing information with their tender that is used to prepare for Stage Two assessments.
- The *Contractor* names their *key persons* with their tender, and may not change them during Stage One except for specified reasons.
- The *Contractor* provides regular forecasts of the Defined Cost for Stage One work for submission to the *Project Manager*, who can accept or not accept the forecast, quoting specified reasons (clause X22.2(2)).
- The *Contractor* provides regular forecasts of the Project Cost in consultation with the *Project Manager*.
- The *Contractor* submits design proposals for Stage Two to the *Project Manager*, including a forecast of the effect of the design proposal on Project Cost and the Accepted Programme.
- The *Project Manager* decides whether to proceed to Stage Two, and they either (*a*) issue the *Contractor* a notice to proceed or (*b*) issue an instruction to remove the work required in Stage Two from the Scope if they decide not to proceed with Stage Two.
- The *Contractor* is incentivised to keep the Project Cost below the Budget, as it is then paid the *budget incentive* stated in the Contract Data.

As with all contracts that involve early contractor involvement and/or Stage Two design contracts, the *Client* may have difficulty with

- providing objective evaluation criteria
- evaluating commercial tenders robustly and comprehensively

and, therefore,

- evidencing good value-for-money proposals.

2.9.1.22 Option Y(UK)1 – the Project Bank Account

If the *Client* wants to make payment to the *Contractor* and any suppliers that they name through a Project Bank Account, Option Y(UK)1 sets out the procedures to be applied:

- The *Client* may choose to pay any charges made by the *project bank* and also then to be paid any interest paid by the *project bank*, and this choice will be stated in Contract Data part one.
- It is the *Contractor* who provides the name of the *project bank* and the *named suppliers* in their Contract Data part two. Named Suppliers are likely to contracted with the *Contractor* or perhaps a Subcontractor to provide part of the *works*.
- The *Contractor* sets up the Project Bank Account and arranges for the Named Suppliers to be a part of the scheme.
- The Trust Deed is signed by the *Client*, the *Contractor* and the Named Suppliers.
- Any new supplier who is to become a Named Supplier joins the scheme through the Joining Deed, which must be completed and signed by the *Client*, the *Contractor* and the new supplier.
- The *Project Manager* accepts details of the banking arrangement submitted by the *Contractor*, or does not accept them for stated reasons.
- Payment procedures are set out: for example, the *Contractor* includes in their application for payment the amount due to Named Suppliers; the *Client* authorises payment to be made to the *Contractor* and the Named Suppliers.

2.9.1.23 Option Y(UK)2 – the Housing Grants, Construction and Regeneration Act 1996

Option Y(UK)2 covers use of the HGCR Act (Part II) with the ECC. This Option was prepared solely for use on contracts that are subject to the HGCR Act; that is, for contracts that fall under the definition of a construction contract under the Act.

The two principles contained in the HGCR Act are those related to payment and adjudication. If a contract is subject to the act, the *Client* will choose Option W2 to cover the adjudication aspect of the Act, and Option Y(UK)2 to cover the payment aspect of the act. If Option Y(UK)2 was not chosen as part of the contract strategy, then the Scheme for Construction Contracts is read into the contract to account for the payment and adjudication changes required by the HGCR Act.

Option Y(UK)2 refers only to payment, and it refers to those payment procedures that are not already included in core clause section 5.

2.9.1.24 Option Y(UK)3 – the Contracts (Rights of Third Parties) Act 1999

Option Y(UK)3 covers the Contracts (Rights of Third Parties) Act 1999 for use with the ECC when used in England and Wales, and may be deemed useful when a central body procures a contract on behalf of others. The legislation can be imported into contracts taking place in Scotland.

2.9.1.25 Option Z – *additional conditions of contract*

Option Z introduces *additional conditions of contract*, with the caveat that any changes to the core clauses should be carefully considered. Because there are no cross-references within the ECC *conditions of contract*, a ready knowledge of the ECC is required before clauses are amended. Option Z should not be used to change the core clauses of the contract so as to introduce onerous and adversarial terms and conditions. Option Z may be used for additional conditions such as confidentiality (particularly to do with the Freedom of Information Act 2000 for public sector bodies in the UK) or boundary conditions that are not included in the core clauses.

Examples

Z2 The second sentence of clause 43.2 is deleted and replaced as follows: 'This period begins when the Defect is notified.'

Z3 Clause 60.1(4) is deleted and replaced with the following: 'The *Project Manager* gives an instruction to stop or not to start any work or change a Key Date except where the instruction relates to health and safety matters or is in relation to a *Contractor* default.'

Z4 The *Contractor* submits their valid tax invoice 7 days after the date of the payment certificate. Where the *Contractor* does not submit their valid tax invoice within the time required, the period within which payment is made and the time allowed in clause 91.4 are extended by the length of time from the date when the *Contractor* should have submitted their valid tax invoice to the date when it does submit it.

Note: these examples are examples only, and do not represent recommendations by the authors. All changes to the *conditions of contract* should be vetted by the *Client's* legal representatives.

Procuring an Engineering and Construction Contract
ISBN 978-0-7277-6184-2

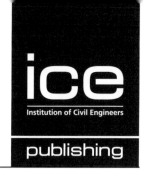

Appendix 3

Inspection of the *Contractor's* accounts and records plan

Section A: Inspection of the *Contractor*'s accounts and records plan – generally

A3.1. Introduction

This plan has been produced to inspect the account and records of the Defined Costs for the *works* undertaken using the Engineering and Construction Contract Option C (Target Contract with Activity Schedule)/Option D (Target Contract with Bill of Quantities)/Option E (Cost Reimbursable Contract).

The Engineering and Construction Contract provides that the *Contractor* is paid the Price for Work Done to Date plus other amounts to be paid to the *Contractor*, less amounts to be paid by or retained from the *Contractor* (clause 50.3).

Under Option C (Target Contract with Activity Schedule)/Option D (Target Contract with Bill of Quantities)/Option E (Cost Reimbursable Contract), the Price for Work Done to Date is

- the total Defined Cost that the Project Manager forecasts will have been paid by the Contractor before the next assessment date plus the Fee (clause 11.2(31)).

This Inspection Plan is designed to demonstrate that the assessment of the *Contractor's* Defined Cost has been completed in accordance with the provisions of the *conditions of contract* and satisfies the requirements of third-party or external inspectors.

The *Client*, the *Project Manager* and the *Contractor* (called the Project Team for the purposes of this Inspection Plan) are jointly committed to ensuring the control of Defined Cost on the *works*. This commitment is reinforced by their joint liability for any over-run of Defined Cost provided by the share mechanism in the *conditions of contract* (for Options C and D).

The Project Team shall operate the procedures within this plan.

A3.2. Basis of Inspection of the *Contractor's* accounts and records plan and procedures

This procedure is devised on the basis that there is a joint commitment towards minimising costs due to the target cost and incentive schemes incorporated within the contract. With the joint incentive to minimise the cost, relatively uncomplicated inspection procedures could be adopted. This Inspection Plan avoids the need for inspecting all costs and endeavours to minimise the cost of implementing the procedures.

There is a need for a number of inspection procedures to be established to meet the inspection objectives and also to satisfy the requirements of third-party or external inspectors.

The Inspection Plan has been established to review administration and management procedures that are in place to manage the costs.

A3.3. Main inspection objectives

The intention of the Inspection Plan is to allow an inspector appointed from the Project Team to provide a monthly report based on a systematic analysis of the records of Defined Cost. This report is intended to provide the Project Team with the maximum confidence in the accuracy of the Defined Cost paid while employing the minimum practical resource to implement the procedures.

The Inspection Plan is divided into seven key inspection task sections:

1 Subcontractors
2 People
3 Equipment
4 Plant and Materials
5 Charges
6 Manufacture and Fabrication
7 Design.

A3.4. Reporting

The *Project Manager*, as a result of carrying out the inspection, shall generate a number of reports/comments. An example of a pro forma 'Inspection Comment Sheet' is given in Figure A3.1.

Reports shall highlight anomalies as well as items that need further action; however, the *Project Manager* shall, when requested, use their professional experience to provide comments/recommendations for consideration by others, which are intended to assist in the management of the *works*. Part of the pre-contract Section 2 – Subcontractors has been specifically drawn up for this purpose.

A3.5. Inspection report

Each section refers to the issue of an inspection report, which is closed out when it has been signed-off by a number of personnel.

Recommendations contained in inspection reports will undoubtedly provide part direction to the inspection tasks for subsequent period inspections.

The Inspection Plan will also need to be reviewed on a regular basis. Objectives and procedures shall be scrutinised by the inspector, and comments and observations will be welcomed from the Project Team. Due to this, a further inspection section is included that will allow comments to be recorded and amendments to be made to the Inspection Plan itself.

Comments and proposals to amend the Inspection Plan shall be discussed and agreed by the *Project Manager* and the *Client's* and *Contractor's* commercial managers.

A3.6. Goals

Each month the *Project Manager* shall set the 'goals' of the Inspection Plan for the next month. This shall be based upon

- meeting the main inspection objectives
- recommendations/comments arising from previous monthly inspection reports
- total workload levels for the month.

The *Project Manager* shall endeavour to work to a strict timetable in order to meet the inspection objective and goals, and it is vital, therefore, that information from the Project Team is provided as rapidly as possible and without hindrance.

A3.7. Amendments to the Inspection Plan

The Inspection Plan is divided into eight sections. These are drafted to enable each section to be self-contained, and therefore general information is included within each section.

The Inspection Plan shall be given a new revision letter upon amendment.

A3.8. Distribution of the Inspection Plan

The Inspection Plan shall be distributed by the inspector to the Project Team, the *Client's* and *Contractor's* head offices, and any third-party or external inspectors at the request of the *Project Manager*.

Figure A3.1 The Inspection Comment Sheet

Inspection comment sheet

Contract title:
Project reference No.:

Client:
Project Manager :
Supervisor :
Contractor:

Details of inspection
[*Description of inspection to be carried out*]

Date of inspection: Auditor:
[*Insert date*]   [*Insert name*]

Inspection findings:

Auditor ....   Date ....

Copies to:						

Section B: Subcontractors

Subcontractors are as defined in clause 11.2(19) of the *conditions of contract*.

B3.1. Inspection objectives

The Subcontractor inspection objectives are divided into (1) Pre-Award and Award and (2) Post-Award tasks to verify that

1 Pre-Award and Award:
   - Subcontract tender documentation is accurate and
   - contractually fair and reasonable
   - competitive prices are obtained
   - Subcontracts are fairly awarded.
2 Post-Award:
   - subcontracts are properly administered
   - assessments of the amounts due to Subcontractors are fair and reasonable
   - final accounts are completed.

B3.1.1 Pre-Award and Award

When requested by the Project Team, the inspection shall be undertaken to

1 confirm compilation of the proposed subcontract tender list
2 verify
   - consistency in contractual terms between the various subcontract tenders issued for this project
   - that tenders are based on latest design and programme information
   - that terms and conditions are fair and reasonable, take cognisance of the main contract conditions and comply with current legislation regarding subcontracts
   - that reasonable price breakdowns have been requested
3 confirm that subcontract tender enquiries are competitively sought or determine reasons for single-tender action
4 confirm that subcontract tenders are sent out and received back and opened at the same time
5 confirm that tenders are being sought at an appropriate time and that tender periods are reasonable
6 confirm that tender returns are compared reasonably and that tender qualifications are withdrawn as far as possible
7 confirm that tenders have been fairly assessed and that the most value-for-money option has generally been accepted (taking cognisance of any outstanding qualifications)
8 confirm that there is full disclosure of discounts
9 confirm that the tender to be accepted has a reasonable breakdown of prices to facilitate evaluation of compensation events
10 confirm that the tenders are awarded on the basis of the latest information.

B3.1.2 Post-Award

The inspection shall be undertaken to verify the following:

1 Changes to the subcontract are being instructed properly in a timely manner and procedures are in place to ensure that Subcontractors have the latest Scope and Site Information issued by the Project Manager.
2 Payments made to Subcontractors are based on the subcontract conditions of contract or where non-Engineering and Construction Subcontract are based on
   - work done and/or materials on Site
   - subcontract rates and prices
   - reasonable rates and prices (in respect of compensation events where subcontract rates and prices do not apply).
3 All payments prepared by the Contractor are for work carried out or for materials supplied for this project and do not include Disallowed Cost.
4 Payments made to Subcontractors align with payments made to the Contractor for the same purpose.

B3.2. Procedures
B3.2.1 Generally

The *Project Manager* shall be supplied with or given access to all information necessary for compliance with the procedures contained within this plan.

■ Inspection Objectives B.1.1.1 and B.1.1.3.
■ For subcontract enquiries issued on this project, the *Project Manager* shall be provided with a signed-off list of tenderers.
■ Reasons for single-tender actions shall be provided.

B3.2.2 Inspection Objectives B.1.1.2, B.1.1.4 and B.1.1.5

1 For all subcontract enquiries to be issued on this project, the *Project Manager* shall be provided with a copy of the draft tender documentation. The *Project Manager* shall undertake a spot check of the documentation within five working days of receipt. The inspector shall verify that the tender documentation
   – includes the latest drawings by reference to the Project Team's document control records
   – is based upon the Engineering and Construction Subcontract or the *Contractor's* standard form of subcontract
   – is consistent for all enquiries, and main contractual terms are relevant and clear.
2 The review by the *Project Manager* shall not be allowed to delay/affect the issuing of the enquiry documents.
3 The *Project Manager* shall be provided with any subsequently issued documents detailing
   – any amendments made to the draft tender documents or price
   – amendments to be made but currently excluded and how they are to be incorporated in the future.

Note: the Project Team should carry out detailed checks on the accuracy and quality of the enquiry documentation.

B3.2.3 Inspection Objectives B.1.1.6 to B.1.1.10

1 For all subcontract enquiries to be issued on this project, the inspector shall receive an initial summary of the tender offers, together with a summary of any qualifications included therein.
2 The Project Team shall assess the tenders in more detail, endeavour to remove qualifications and send the inspector a copy of their recommendation together with their reconciliation of prices and qualifications.
3 Within five working days of receipt, providing this date is before the date required for award, the inspector may review documents and provide any comments on the recommendation to the Project Team.

B3.2.4 Inspection Objective B.1.2.1

1 When requested by the *Project Manager*, the Project Team shall provide a schedule listing all instructions issued to Subcontractors.
2 The *Project Manager* shall carry out random checks by comparison with the Project Team's document control records.

B3.2.5 Inspection Objectives B.1.2.2 and B.1.2.3

1 The *Project Manager* shall carry out spot checks on payment certificates. When requested by the inspector, the Project Team shall provide a copy of the latest payment certificate together with a breakdown of the latest or previous valuations as may be necessary.
2 The *Project Manager* may request further support documentation such as
   – site notes/measurements
   – measurements from drawings/final accounts
   – build-ups for new rates
   – copies of subcontract documentation
   – delivery tickets
   – schedule of Disallowed Costs.
3 The inspector shall carry out spot checks to verify that
   – rates or prices used are contract rates or prices or compatible therewith
   – work has been executed in relation to this project
   – the value included for materials relates to materials on Site for this project
   – the value of compensation events is identified
   – consideration has been made for Disallowed Costs.
4 On completion of the draft final account, the *Project Manager* may review the final account and carry out spot checks as referred to above.

B3.2.6 Inspection Objectives B.1.2.4	The *Project Manager* shall carry out spot checks that payments made to the *Contractor* in respect of Subcontractors have also been made to the Subcontractors.
B3.3. Inspection records **B3.3.1 Generally**	Full inspection records of Subcontractors shall be kept and filed in accordance with this procedure.

B3.3.2 Monthly Subcontractor Inspection Report

The *Project Manager* shall issue a Subcontractor Inspection Report to the Project Team on a monthly basis. It shall identify positive findings as well as items needing further action and consideration.

The Subcontractor Inspection Report shall not be deemed completed until it has been signed off by

- the inspector
- the *Project Manager* or their authorised representative
- the *Contractor* or their authorised representative.

B3.3.3 Subcontractor Record of Inspection

The Record of Inspection is prepared by the inspector to record all tasks undertaken since the cut-off date of the previous Subcontractor Inspection Report. It is retained by the inspector for review by the Project Team and third-party or external inspectors.

The Record of Inspection shall be the backup document to the Subcontractor Inspection Report.

B3.3.4 Filing

A file shall be established entitled '[Project Name] – Subcontractor Inspection Records'.

B3.3.5 Timescales

The inspector shall initially carry out an inspection for the month of [month] [year]. Subsequent inspections shall be carried out on a monthly basis.

Section C: People

Defined Cost relating to People is described in section 1 of the Schedule of Cost Components.

C3.1. Inspection objectives

Examination of individual payslips of persons who are paid in full (or in part) on a time basis to verify that

- payslips tie up with a weekly payroll summary provided by the *Contractor*
- rates of pay are in accordance with conditions of employment
- payslips relate to labour allocation/timesheets
- payments relate to work executed on this project.

C3.2. Inspection records
C3.2.1 Generally

- Full inspection records of People shall be kept and filed in accordance with this procedure.
- It is anticipated that the People 'trend' charts as well as the People Inspection Reports will be of use both to the inspector and the Project Team.

C3.2.2 Monthly People Inspection Report

The inspector shall issue a People Inspection Report to the Project Team on a monthly basis. It shall identify positive findings as well as items needing further action and consideration.

The People Inspection Report shall not be deemed completed until it has been signed off by

- the inspector
- the *Project Manager* or their authorised representative
- the *Contractor* or their authorised representative.

C3.2.3 People Record of Inspection

- The Record of Inspection is prepared by the inspector to record all tasks undertaken since the cut-off date of the previous People Inspection Report. It is retained by the inspector for review by the Project Team and third-party or external inspectors.

- The Record of Inspection shall summarise the records examined during the period and it shall note
  - the calendar period
  - the basis of selection
  - the names of People records inspected
  - payroll numbers
  - the grade of labour and work location
  - if allocation sheets/timesheet and swipe card records are consistent
  - if payslips tie up with weekly payroll records.
- The People Record of Inspection shall be signed off by the inspector as a true record, and forms the basis of the Monthly People Inspection Report.

C3.2.4 Trend tables   The trend table(s), which will include the following, shall supplement the Record of Inspection:

- The wage bill for current and previous periods.
- The average labour cost per person per month for this period and previous periods.
- The number of persons employed during this period and previous periods.

C3.2.5 Filing   A file shall be established entitled '[Project Name] – People Inspection Records'.

C3.2.6 Timescales   The inspector shall initially carry out an inspection for the month of [month and year]. Subsequent inspections shall be carried out on a monthly basis.

C3.3. Information to be provided by the Project Team   In order to meet the inspection objectives, the Project Team shall be required to provide information including, but not limited to

- weekly payroll build-up
- payslips
- allocation sheets
- productivity records
- gradings of staff
- agreed rates of pay and basis of agreement
- information from bank statements.

Section D: Equipment

For the purposes of this procedure, Equipment is as defined in clause 11.2(9) of the *conditions of contract*. Defined Cost relating to Equipment is described in section 2 of the Schedule of Cost Components.

D3.1. Inspection objectives   The inspection objectives are divided into two main areas to verify the following:

- Pre-order: that orders or purchases are based upon accurate documentation and competitive prices.
- Post-order: that Equipment orders are properly administered and payments made relate to usage on this project.

D3.1.1 Pre-order
1 Confirm competitive prices have been obtained or used, and where Equipment is hired or purchased from other parts of the *Contractor* group of companies confirm that prices are reasonable.
2 Confirm site indents estimate the periods of hire and that indents have been signed off.

D3.1.2 Post-order
1 Confirm prices for extra periods of hire are generally obtained as set out in the pre-order section or based upon prices previously agreed and obtained competitively.
2 Verify payments made are based upon Equipment hired or purchased, at contract rates and prices, and also relate to Equipment charges arising after [date].
3 Verify Equipment deliveries are checked and align with orders.

4 Check a procedure is in place to ensure Equipment is off-hired in a timely manner.
5 Verify payments made for Equipment align with payments made to the *Contractor* and that payments are made at the appropriate time and that any Disallowed Costs have been taken into account.
6 Check overall capital expenditure costs allow for a residual value of purchased Equipment.

D3.2. Procedures
D3.2.1 Inspection Objectives D.1.1.1, D.1.2.1 and D.1.2.6

- The inspector shall review a list of Equipment orders placed.
- The inspector shall select orders and view documentation and resulting reports and recommendations, spot check that competitive prices have been received and that costs incurred relate to this project.
- Where Equipment is hired or purchased from a company within the same group of companies as the *Contractor*, the inspector shall be provided with details of competitive rates and prices and that hire rates for specialist Equipment make due consideration for working life/residual value.

D3.2.2 Inspection Objective D.1.1.2

- The inspector shall select orders at random and view requisitions relating thereto.
- The inspector shall carry out spot checks to verify that
  - requisitions have been signed off in accordance with the relevant procedure
  - requisitions and Equipment orders identify the estimated period of hire
  - orders are sanctioned by the delegated person within the Project Team.

D3.2.3 Inspection Objectives D.1.2.1, D.1.2.2 and D.1.2.3

- The inspector shall select orders at random and review relevant delivery notes to ascertain that Equipment has been checked and received and is intended for use on this project.
- The inspector shall select orders at random to carry out spot checks. These checks shall include checking that payments are compatible with deliveries, periods of hire and invoices received; and also that the correct rates have been used for calculation of payment due, all discounts are disclosed and that periods of additional hire are backed up by revised requisitions based on Site assessments.

D3.2.4 Inspection Objective D.1.2.4

- The inspector shall carry out spot checks to determine that procedures are in place to monitor the use of/need for Equipment and that Equipment is being returned in a timely manner.
- The inspector shall check requisition forms and compare these with monitoring procedures.

D3.2.5 Inspection Objective D.1.2.5

- The inspector shall spot check that amounts certified by the Project Team align with total payments made in respect of Equipment.

D3.3. Inspection records
D3.3.1 Generally

Full inspection records of Equipment shall be kept and filed in accordance with this procedure.

D3.3.2 Equipment Inspection Report

The inspector shall issue an Equipment Inspection Report to the Project Team on a monthly basis. It shall identify positive findings as well as items needing further action and consideration.

The Equipment Inspection Report shall not be deemed completed until it has been signed off by

- the inspector
- the *Project Manager* or their authorised representative
- the *Contractor* or their authorised representative.

D3.3.3 Equipment Record of Inspection

- The Record of Inspection is prepared by the inspector to record all tasks undertaken since the cut-off date of the previous Equipment Inspection Report. It is retained by the inspector for review by the Project Team and third-party or external inspectors.
- The Record of Inspection shall summarise the records examined during the period and it shall note
  - the calendar period
  - the basis of selection

    – the items of Equipment inspected
    – Equipment identification numbers
    – if requisitions correlate with orders and invoices
    – if procedures for off-hiring Equipment have been operated in the period.

■ The Equipment Record of Inspection shall be signed off by the inspector as a true record, and forms the basis of the Monthly Equipment Inspection Report.

D3.3.4 Filing

A file shall be established entitled '[project name] – Equipment Inspection Records'.

D3.3.5 Timescales

The inspector shall initially carry out an inspection for the month of [month] [year]. Subsequent inspections shall be carried out on a monthly basis.

D3.4. Information to be provided by the Project Team

In order to meet these objectives, the Project Team shall be required to provide information including, but not limited to

■ a list of orders raised and estimated values
■ a summary of payments made in the period
■ quotations from suppliers
■ access to invoices and delivery note records
■ a schedule of total Equipment on Site
■ assessments/recommendations carried out by Project Team prior to placing orders
■ site assessment of schedules of Equipment.

Section E: Plant and Materials

For the purposes of this procedure, Plant and Materials are as defined in clause 11.2(14) of the *conditions of contract*. Defined Cost relating to Plant and Materials is described in section 3 of the Schedule of Cost Components.

E3.1. Inspection objectives

The inspection objectives are divided into two main areas to verify the following:

■ Pre-order: that orders are based upon accurate documentation and competitive prices are obtained.
■ Post-order: that Plant and Materials orders are properly administered and that payments are accurate and timely.

E3.1.1 Pre-order

1 Confirm competitive prices are obtained.
2 Confirm orders are, where applicable, based upon a reasonable assessment of quantities using the latest Scope and Site Information.
3 Confirm a maximum order value based upon quantities is ascertained and recorded.
4 Confirm orders detail payment periods and terms.
5 Confirm the final location of Plant and Materials can be identified from the order and requisition.
6 Confirm details on orders match those on the requisition raising the order.

E3.1.2 Post-order

1 Verify payments made are based upon Plant and Materials delivered and agreed rates and that payments exclude any Disallowed Cost.
2 Verify Plant and Materials delivery notes are being accurately checked.
3 Verify total delivery of Plant and Materials corresponds with orders.
4 Confirm payments made for Plant and Materials align with payments made to the *Contractor* for same purpose and payments are made at the appropriate time.

E3.2. Procedures
E3.2.1 Inspection Objectives E.1.1.1 and E.1.1.5

■ The inspector shall select orders and view indents and order forms and verify that competitive prices have been received and that the location for Plant and Materials can be ascertained.
■ The basis of selection shall be recorded.

E3.2.2 Inspection Objective E.1.1.2

- The inspector shall select an order at random and review quantities against drawing numbers referred to in the order.
- The inspector shall carry out spot checks to determine that
  - the latest drawings have been used
  - quantities have been used as the basis for enquiries and can be ascertained from the drawings.

Note: the inspector will not carry out detailed checks on the quantities and orders, as the Project Team shall carry this out.

E3.2.3 Inspection Objective E.1.1.3

- The inspector shall carry out spot checks that maximum prices recorded coincide with tenders received.

E3.2.4 Inspection Objective E.1.1.4

- The inspector shall carry out spot checks on selected enquiries and orders to determine whether payment terms/payment periods are recorded and reasonable.

E3.2.5 Inspection Objective E.1.1.5

- The inspector shall carry out spot checks on selected orders to determine whether requisition details match those on orders.

E3.2.6 Inspection Objectives E.1.2.1, E.1.2.2 and E.1.2.3

- The inspector shall select orders and request access to delivery notes and invoices and shall carry out spot checks using selected delivery notes to ascertain that Plant and Materials have been received and checked and that a reconciliation has been carried out against the order.
- The inspector shall select orders to carry out spot checks that payments made are consistent with actual deliveries made and that correct rates have been used for this purpose, and that all discounts are disclosed.

E3.2.7 Inspection Objective E.1.2.4

- The inspector shall carry out spot checks that amounts certified by the Project Team for payment align with total payments made.

E3.3. Inspection records

E3.3.1 Generally

Full inspection records of Plant and Materials shall be kept and filed in accordance with this procedure.

E3.3.2 Plant and Materials Inspection Report

The inspector shall issue a Plant and Materials Inspection Report to the Project Team on a monthly basis. It shall identify positive findings as well as items needing further action and consideration.

The Plant and Materials Inspection Report shall not be deemed completed until it has been signed off by

- the inspector
- the *Project Manager* or their authorised representative
- the *Contractor* or their authorised representative.

E3.3.3 Plant and Materials Record of Inspection

- The Record of Inspection is prepared by the inspector to record all tasks undertaken since the cut-off date of the previous Plant and Materials Inspection Report. It is retained by the inspector for review by the Project Team and third-party or external inspectors.
- The Record of Inspection shall summarise the records examined during the period and it shall note
  - the calendar period
  - the basis of selection
  - items of Plant and Materials inspected
  - if requisitions correlate with orders and invoices.
- The Plant and Materials Record of Inspection shall be signed off by the inspector as a true record, and forms the basis of the Monthly Plant and Materials Inspection Report.

E3.3.4 Filing

A file shall be established entitled '[project name] – Plant and Materials Inspection Records'.

E3.3.5 Timescales

The inspector shall initially carry out an Inspection for the month of [month and year]. Subsequent inspections shall be carried out on a monthly basis.

E3.4. Information to be provided by the Project Team

In order to meet these objectives, the Project Team shall be required to provide information including, but not limited to

- Plant and Materials requisitions
- the list of orders raised and values of orders
- the register of delivery notes for the period and access to invoices and records
- invoices received.

Section F: Charges

For the purposes of this procedure, Defined Cost relating to Charges is described in section 4 of the Schedule of Cost Components.

F3.1. Inspection Objectives

F3.1.1 Random examination of payments

This is done to verify that

- a comprehensive build-up is available
- where applicable, costs are based upon quotes/invoices/scale charges/fair rates and that costs exclude Disallowed Cost
- costs need to be incurred to carry out the *works*
- costs relate to this project.

F3.1.2 Spot checks on overall costs

These are to

- compare site costing records against actual pay records sent from the *Contractor*
- record cost trends.

F3.2. Procedures

F3.2.1 Generally

- Due to the nature of the contract, it is impractical to check all records of charges, and the inspection must therefore necessarily be selective.

F3.2.2 Inspection Objective F1.1

- The inspector shall select one or more payments in the inspection period.
- The inspector shall determine and record the basis of selection.
- The inspector shall inspect the *Contractor's* build-up to the payment to ensure it is comprehensive and excludes any Disallowed Cost.
- The inspector shall also select individual costs in the build-ups. The *Contractor* shall provide evidence of the basis of order and payment and to ascertain if prices are based on competitive rates/scale charges or fair rates.

F3.2.3 Inspection Objective F1.2

- The total costs for charges are spot checked against actual records sent from the *Contractor*.
- A trend table is produced, comparing expenditure for different periods.
- The *Contractor* shall on a monthly basis break down the expenditure into agreed heads of charge. The inspector shall check costs and enter them into a trend table, comparing expenditure on a monthly basis.

F3.3. Inspection records

F3.3.1 Generally

- Full inspection records of charges shall be kept and filed in accordance with this procedure.
- It is anticipated that the trend tables will be of use to both the inspector and the Project Team.

F3.3.2 Charges Inspection Report

The inspector shall issue a Charges Inspection Report to the Project Team on a monthly basis. It shall identify positive findings as well as items needing further action and consideration.

The Charges Inspection Report shall not be deemed completed until it has been signed off by

- the inspector
- the *Project Manager* or their authorised representative
- the *Contractor* or their authorised representative.

F3.3.3 Charges Record of Inspection

- The Record of Inspection is prepared by the inspector to record all tasks undertaken since the cut-off date of the previous Charges Inspection Report. It is retained by the inspector for review by the Project Team and third-party or external inspectors.
- The Record of Inspection shall summarise the records examined during the period and it shall note
  - the calendar period
  - the basis of selection
  - if payments correlate with orders and invoices.
- The Charges Record of Inspection shall be signed off by the inspector as a true record, and forms the basis of the Monthly Charges Inspection Report.

F3.3.4 Trend tables

The trend table(s), which will include the following, shall supplement the Record of Inspection.

- The total cost for current and previous periods.
- The total cost for current and previous periods in agreed head of charge.

F3.3.5 Filing

A file shall be established entitled '[project name] – Charges Inspection Records'.

F3.3.6 Timescales

The inspector shall initially carry out an inspection for the month of [month] [year]. Subsequent inspections shall be carried out on a monthly basis.

F3.4. Information to be provided by the Project Team

In order to meet these objectives, the Project Team shall be required to provide information including, but not limited to

- the monthly build-up of costs broken down into heads of charge
- agreed rates of pay/quotations/invoices, etc.

Section G: Manufacture and Fabrication

For the purposes of this procedure, Defined Cost relating to Manufacture and Fabrication is described in section 6 of the Schedule of Cost Components.

G3.1. Inspection objectives
G3.1.1 Examination of the build-up to payments

This is done to confirm that

- the value of Equipment and Plant and Materials is in agreement with contract values
- the calculation of price adjustment factor is correct
- the date for completion of Manufacture and Fabrication of Equipment and Plant and Materials is agreed with the designated member of the Project Team.

G3.1.2 Visit the site of Manufacture and Fabrication

This is done to

- confirm items of Equipment and Plant and Materials included in payment are complete
- verify that Equipment and Plant and Materials are marked in accordance with the procedures described in the Scope (clause 71.1).

G3.2. Procedures
G3.2.1 Generally

- The inspector shall be supplied with or given access to all information necessary for compliance with the procedures contained within this plan.
- The inspector shall be allowed access to all sites where Equipment and Plant and Materials are stored outside the Working Areas, having given due notice of their intention to make an inspection.

G3.2.2 Inspection Objective G1.1

- The inspector shall be provided with calculations detailing the build-up to sums included in payments for Manufacture and Fabrication outside the Working Areas.
- The inspector shall be provided with a notification confirming the date of completion of Manufacture and Fabrication of Equipment and Plant and Materials.

G3.2.3 Inspection Objective G1.2	■ The inspector shall visit the site of Manufacture and Fabrication outside the Working Areas to view completed Equipment and Plant and Materials, and check that items are marked in accordance with the procedures described in the Scope.

G3.3. Inspection records
G3.3.1 Generally

Full inspection records of Manufacture and Fabrication shall be kept and filed in accordance with this procedure.

G3.3.2 Charges Inspection Report

The inspector shall issue a Manufacture and Fabrication Inspection Report to the Project Team on a monthly basis. It shall identify positive findings as well as items needing further action and consideration.

The Manufacture and Fabrication Inspection Report shall not be deemed completed until it has been signed off by

■ the inspector
■ the *Project Manager* or their authorised representative
■ the *Contractor* or their authorised representative.

G3.3.3 Charges Record of Inspection

■ The Record of Inspection is prepared by the inspector to record all tasks undertaken since the cut-off date of the previous Manufacture and Fabrication Inspection Report. It is retained by the inspector for review by the Project Team and third-party or external inspectors.
■ The Record of Inspection shall summarise the records examined during the period and it shall note
 – the calendar period
 – the basis of selection
 – if payments correlate with orders and invoices.
■ The Manufacture and Fabrication Record of Inspection shall be signed off by the inspector as a true record, and forms the basis of the Monthly Manufacture and Fabrication Inspection Report.

G3.3.4 Filing

A file shall be established entitled '[project name] – Manufacture and Fabrication Inspection Records'.

G3.3.5 Timescales

The inspector shall initially carry out an inspection for the month of [month] [year]. Subsequent inspections shall be carried out on a monthly basis.

Section H: Design

For the purposes of this procedure, Defined Cost relating to design is described in section 7 of the Schedule of Cost Components.

H3.1. Inspection objectives
H3.1.1 Examination of payslips (time basis)

Examination of individual payslips of persons who are paid in full (or in part) on a time basis to verify that

■ payslips tie up with a weekly payroll summary provided by the *Contractor*
■ rates of pay are in accordance with conditions of employment
■ payslips relate to labour allocation/timesheets
■ payments relate to work executed on this project.

H3.1.2 Examination of payslips (productivity basis)

Examination of individual payslips of persons paid in full (or in part) on a productivity basis to verify that

■ payslips tie up with weekly payroll summary provided by the *Contractor*
■ productivity payments tie up with productivity records.

H3.1.3 Examination of consistency

Examination to confirm consistency between labour allocation sheets and the swipe card checking on/off system.

H3.1.4 Spot checks on labour costs

Spot checks on overall labour costs to

- compare Site costing records against actual pay records provided by the *Contractor*
- calculate the average labour cost per person-week for the period
- calculate the average hourly cost for the period
- produce trend tables to show changes in costs and workforce levels
- ensure that Disallowed Costs have not been included in payments.

H3.2. Procedures
H3.2.1 Generally

Due to the nature of the contract, it is impractical to check the pay records of all design personnel employed by the *Contractor* on the project. The inspection, therefore, must be based on a selective cross-section that is representative of the Defined Cost incurred.

H3.2.2 Inspection Objectives H1.1 and H1.2

- The inspector shall determine the time periods to be inspected and select names from the list of design personnel employed on the Project.
- The inspector shall determine and record the basis of selection.
- The inspector shall inspect their allocation sheets/timesheets to ensure there are no discrepancies. The rates of pay shall be checked against a list of rates of pay and sundry information determined from the conditions of employment provided by the *Contractor*.
- Any overtime payments or travelling and subsistence payments are also checked for accuracy against the basis for calculation of such payment provided by the *Contractor*.
- Payslips are also compared with weekly payroll summaries.

H3.2.3 Inspection Objective H1.3

- The inspector shall determine the time periods to be inspected and shall select names from the list of design personnel employed on the project.
- The inspector shall determine or record the basis of selection.
- The inspector shall inspect allocation sheets to check they have been signed off by an authorised representative of the Project Team.

H3.2.4 Inspection Objective H1.4

The inspector shall determine the time period to be inspected and how regularly calculations are to be made, and use the total Defined Cost of Design to

- check the actual pay records supplied by the *Contractor*
- calculate the average employee cost per person per week during the period and enter this into a 'trend' chart
- calculate the average hourly cost during the period and enter this into a 'trend' chart
- calculate the total number of persons employed and enter this into a 'trend' chart
- check to ensure any Disallowed Costs have not been paid.

H3.3. Inspection records
H3.3.1 Generally

- Full inspection records of design shall be kept and filed in accordance with this procedure.
- It is anticipated that the design 'trend' charts as well as the Design Inspection Reports shall be of use both to the inspector and the Project Team.

H3.3.2 Monthly Design Inspection Report

The inspector shall issue a Design Inspection Report to the Project Team on a monthly basis. It shall identify positive findings as well as items needing further action and consideration.

The Design Inspection Report shall not be deemed completed until it has been signed off by

- the inspector
- the *Project Manager* or their authorised representative
- the *Contractor* or their authorised representative.

H3.3.3 Design Record of Inspection

- The Record of Inspection is prepared by the inspector to record all tasks undertaken since the cut-off date of the previous Design Inspection Report. It is retained by the inspector for review by the Project Team and third-party or external inspectors.

■ The Record of Inspection shall summarise the records examined during the period and it shall note
  – the calendar period
  – the basis of selection
  – the names of design personnel records inspected
  – payroll numbers
  – the grade of employees and work location
  – if payslips tie up with weekly payroll records.
■ The Design Record of Inspection shall be signed off by the inspector as a true record, and forms the basis of the Monthly Design Inspection Report.

H3.3.4 Trend tables

The trend table(s), which will include the following, shall supplement the Record of Inspection.

■ The wage bill for current and previous periods.
■ The average labour cost per person per month for this period and previous periods.
■ The number of persons employed during this period and previous periods.

H3.3.5 Filing

A file shall be established entitled '[project name] – Design Inspection Records'.

H3.3.6 Timescales

The inspector shall initially carry out an inspection for the month of [month] [year]. Subsequent inspections shall be carried out on a monthly basis.

H3.4. Information to be provided by the Project Team

In order to meet the inspection objectives, the Project Team shall be required to provide information including, but not limited to

■ the weekly payroll build-up
■ payslips
■ allocation sheets
■ productivity records
■ the grading of employees
■ agreed rates of pay and the basis of agreement
■ information from bank statements.

Procuring an Engineering and Construction Contract
ISBN 978-0-7277-6184-2

ICE Publishing: All rights reserved
http://dx.doi.org/10.1680/pecc.61842.083

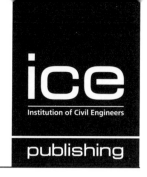

Chapter 3
Completing the Contract Data

Synopsis

This chapter gives guidance on

- how to choose a main Option
- how to choose an Option for resolving and avoiding disputes
- how to choose secondary Options
- choosing optional statements in the Contract Data
- where to position the optional statements in the Contract Data
- how to complete each statement in the Contract Data.

3.1. Introduction

The Contract Data should not be copied from previous contracts but should instead be considered carefully for each new contract that is drafted, taking into account the specific circumstances of the project.

The following information is designed to assist you in completing the Contract Data, by asking the questions you will need to answer before you can complete the Contract Data.

The Contract Data represents the *Client's* contract strategy included in their invitation to tender documentation and the *Contractor's* tender, and therefore forms the heart of an ECC contract. The same questions should be asked for each and every contract to ensure that appropriate choices are made and to ensure that the contract strategy suits the particular project.

Note that the chapter refers to the Contract Data in the ECC, and therefore it refers to both Contract Data part one by the *Client* and Contract Data part two by the *Contractor*. The information can just as easily be used by the *Contractor* for the Engineering and Construction Subcontract, where Contract Data part one is by the *Contractor* and Contract Data part two is by the Subcontractor.

3.2. Structure of the chapter

The columns of the table in section 3.4.1 below contain the following information:

- Column A: a question that needs to be answered.
- Column B: comments indicating how the Contract Data is affected by your answer.
- Column C: a replication of the Contract Data item that the question affects, so that you know which part of the Contract Data to complete.

The structure of this chapter is as follows:

- Part 1 of the chapter asks questions about how you want to pay the *Contractor* (or the Subcontractor for an Engineering and Construction Subcontract contract) during the period of the contract, guiding you to a choice of main Option.
- Part 2 of the chapter asks questions about how you want to resolve and avoid disputes, guiding you in your choice of Option W1, W2 or W3.
- Part 3 of the chapter asks further questions about the contract strategy for the particular project, guiding you in your choice of secondary Options.
- Part 4 of the chapter continues with questions about your chosen contract strategy, guiding you in choices about the optional statements that appear within the body of the Contract Data.
- Part 5 of the chapter describes each entry in Contract Data part one by the *Client*, referring back to the contract strategy chosen through answering earlier questions in parts one, two and three above.
- Part 6 of the chapter describes each entry in Contract Data part two by the *Contractor* (or the Subcontractor in the Engineering and Construction Subcontract), referring back to the contract strategy chosen through answering earlier questions.

Secondary Options in the ECC			
X1	Price adjustment for inflation	X15	The *Contractor's* design
X2	Changes in the law	X16	Retention
X3	Multiple currencies	X17	Low performance damages
X4	Ultimate holding company guarantee	X18	Limitation of liability
X5	Sectional Completion	X20	Key Performance Indicators
X6	Bonus for early Completion	X21	Whole life cost
X7	Delay damages	X22	Early *Contractor* involvement
X8	Undertakings to the *Client* or Others	Y(UK)1	Project Bank Account
X9	Transfer of rights	Y(UK)2	The Housing Grants, Construction and Regeneration Act 1996
X10	Information modelling		
X11	Termination by the *Client*	Y(UK)3	The Contracts (Rights of Third Parties) Act 1999
X12	Multiparty collaboration		
X13	Performance bond	Z	*Additional conditions of contract*
X14	Advanced payment to the *Contractor*		

3.3. Part 1 of this chapter: choosing the main Option

This part of the chapter asks questions about how the *Client* wants to pay the *Contractor* during the period of the contract, guiding you to a choice of main Option. The questions apply equally to the *Contractor's* choices in the Engineering and Construction Subcontract, although those choices are normally more restricted.

3.3.1 Contract Data by the *Client*

	Column A Question	Column B Assistance	Column C Contract Data item
1	What is the status of the Scope? How complete is it and how many changes are expected?	**Discussion** The status of the Scope affects the choice of main Option. The more complete the Scope, the more suitable it will be to choose a lump sum contract as the payment mechanism. Other factors affecting the choice of main Option could be the perceived requirement to incentivise the *Contractor*. **Action** Choose the main Option that best matches the status and quality of the Scope and best reflects the project objectives.	■ The *conditions of contract* are the core clauses and the following clauses for the main Option, the Option for resolving and avoiding disputes and secondary Options of the NEC4 Engineering and Construction Contract June 2017 Main Option .... Option for resolving and avoiding disputes .... Secondary Options ....
2	How do you want to pay the *Contractor*, i.e. using a *bill of quantities*, *activity schedule* or Defined Cost?	**Discussion** The main Options A to F give a choice of payment mechanism. Part of the decision to use main Option A or B (or C or D) is a choice of whether to pay according to a *bill of quantities* (remeasurement) or an *activity schedule* (milestone/stage payments). **Action** Options A and C use an *activity schedule* to build up the contract value and the target cost, respectively. Options B and D use a *bill of quantities* to build up the contract value and the target cost, respectively. Options C, D and E all use Defined Cost plus Fee as defined to pay the *Contractor* during the period of the contract, irrespective in the case of C and D of the method of arriving at the target cost.	See Contract Data entries for Options A, B, C, D, E or F in both Contract Data part one and Contract Data part two.

3.4. Part 2 of this chapter: choosing the Option for resolving and avoiding disputes

This part of the chapter asks questions about how the *Client* wants to resolve and avoid disputes with the *Contractor* during the period of the contract, guiding you to a choice of Option W1, W2 or W3. The questions apply equally to the *Contractor's* choices in the Engineering and Construction Subcontract, although those choices are normally more restricted.

Any reference to CD1 is a reference to Contract Data part one by the *Client*. Any reference to CD2 is a reference to Contract Data part two by the *Contractor*.

3.4.1 Contract Data by the *Client*

	Column A Question	Column B Assistance	Column C Contract Data item
3	What method of dispute resolution does the *Client* choose for the last tier of dispute resolution? Complete the relevant statement in Contract Data part one.	**Discussion** In all three Options for resolving and avoiding disputes (W1, W2 and W3), the *tribunal* is the last tier of dispute resolution and avoidance. Usually, the *tribunal* is litigation or arbitration. **Action** Complete the statement in Contract Data part one with the method chosen as the last tier of resolving and avoiding disputes.	■ The *tribunal* is . . . .
4	Has the *Client* chosen arbitration as the last tier of dispute resolution? YES Complete the optional statements in CD1 NO Do nothing	**Discussion** The Contract Data requires information about arbitration to be stated, so if you have chosen arbitration as the *tribunal*, then the arbitration procedure and other elements relating to the arbitration also need to be decided. **Action** If the *tribunal* is arbitration, include the optional statement in Contract Data part one section on resolving and avoiding disputes. If the *tribunal* is litigation, there is no need to include the optional statement relating to arbitration.	**Contract Data part one** ■ The *arbitration procedure* is . . . . ■ The place where arbitration is to be held is . . . . ■ The person or organisation who will choose an *arbitrator* if the Parties cannot agree a choice or if the *arbitration procedure* does not state who selects an arbitrator, is . . . .
5	UK only: does your project fall within the definition of a construction contract in the HGCR Act? YES Choose Option W2 NO Go to question 6	**Discussion** If the *works* fall within the definition of a construction contract and construction operations within the HGCR Act Part II, sections 104 and 105, then the *Client* must choose Option W2 as the applicable Option for resolving and avoiding disputes. The HGCR Act requires that adjudication is the first level of dispute resolution, and the act provides the procedures for any such adjudication (generally called 'statutory adjudication'). If the HGCR Act does apply to the contract, and Option W2 is not chosen, then the default position is described in the Scheme for Construction Contracts (England and Wales) Regulations 1998 and the Scheme for Construction Contracts (Scotland) Regulations 1998. Option W2 provides the option of a more informal first-tier dispute resolution through use of the *Senior Representatives*; but a dispute can still be referred to the *Adjudicator* at any time, in keeping with the HGCR Act. If a Party is dissatisfied with the result of the adjudication, they may choose to take the dispute to the final tier of dispute resolution: the *tribunal*.	**Contract Data part one** ■ The *Senior Representatives* of the *Client* are Name (1) . . . . Address for communications . . . . Address for electronic communications . . . . Name (2) . . . . Address for communications . . . . Address for electronic communications . . . . ■ The *Adjudicator* is Name . . . . Address for communications . . . . Address for electronic communications . . . . ■ The *Adjudicator nominating body* is . . . .

	Column A Question	Column B Assistance	Column C Contract Data item
		Action Choose Option W2 if the *Client* thinks that the contract is a construction contract in accordance with the HGCR Act and it does not want the Scheme for Construction Contracts to apply. Where countries other than the UK have similar acts or schemes in place, these could be incorporated through the use of Option Z.	
6	If the HGCR Act does not apply to the contract, does the *Client* still want to use adjudication as a tier of dispute resolution? YES Choose Option W1 NO Go to question 7	**Discussion** The NEC proposed adjudication as a dispute resolution method before it was mandated by UK law in the HGCR Act. This option is still available for all non-UK projects and all UK projects that do not fall within the definition of a construction contract under the HGCR Act. In Option W1, adjudication becomes the second tier of dispute resolution, and a first tier of dispute resolution must be used prior to adjudication: the *Senior Representatives*. **Action** Where Option W1 is chosen as the Option for resolving and avoiding disputes, the *Client* is required to provide the names and contact details of the *Senior Representatives* for the *Client* and also to provide details for the *Adjudicator*.	**Contract Data part one** ■ The *Senior Representatives* of the *Client* are Name (1) .... Address for communications .... Address for electronic communications .... Name (2) .... Address for communications .... Address for electronic communications .... ■ The *Adjudicator* is Name .... Address for communications .... Address for electronic communications .... ■ The *Adjudicator nominating body* is ....
7	If the *Client* does not want to use adjudication as a tier of dispute resolution, then there is only one Option for resolving and avoiding disputes left to choose: Option W3. If the *Client* does not want to use an Option W3 Dispute Avoidance Board as the first tier of dispute resolution, then the *Client* may wish to not choose any Option W and include an alternative dispute resolution option through Option Z *additional conditions of contract*.	**Discussion** The Dispute Avoidance Board focuses on avoiding and resolving disputes quickly through regular visits to the Site and an objective of attempting to avoid disputes and resolving them quickly through knowledge of the *works*. The choice of a Dispute Avoidance Board could potentially increase the immediate financial cost of the project to both Parties but is unlikely to affect the total cost of the *works* so much that the Parties would opt not to choose Option W3. **Action** Where the *Client* decides that the project would benefit from a Dispute Avoidance Board rather than adjudication, the Contract Data items are completed. Where the *Client* does not want to use any of Options W1, W2 and W3, they may decide not to choose any of the three Options and to include their own method of dispute resolution through describing the procedure using Option Z *additional conditions of contract*.	■ The *Client's* nomination for the Dispute Avoidance Board is Name .... Address for electronic communications .... ■ The Dispute Avoidance Board visit the Site at intervals no longer than .... months ■ The *Dispute Avoidance Board nominating body* is ....

3.4.2 Contract Data provided by the *Contractor*

	Column A Question	Column B Assistance	Column C Contract Data item
8	Has Option W1 or W2 been chosen by the *Client*?	**Discussion** If Option W1 or W2 has been chosen by the *Client*, then the *Contractor* is required to nominate their own *Senior Representatives* as part of dispute resolution. The *Adjudicator* is chosen by the *Client*, and the *Contractor* must accept the choice provided in Contract Data part one. **Action** Complete the required statements in Contract Data part two.	**Contract Data part two** ■ The *Senior Representatives* of the *Contractor* are Name (1) . . . . Address for communications . . . . Address for electronic communications . . . . Name (2) . . . . Address for communications . . . . Address for electronic communications . . . .
9	Has Option W3 been chosen by the *Client*?	**Discussion** If Option W3 has been chosen by the *Client*, then the *Contractor* is required to nominate their own representative on the Dispute Avoidance Board. **Action** Complete the required statement in Contract Data part two.	■ The *Contractor's* nomination for the Dispute Avoidance Board is Name . . . .

3.5. Part 3 of this chapter: choosing the secondary Options

This part of the chapter asks further questions about the *Client's* contract strategy, guiding you to choices about the secondary Options.

Most of the secondary Options could increase the cost of the project to the *Client*. For example, it costs the *Contractor* to provide a performance bond or retention, and they are likely to pass that cost on to the *Client* in some way. By offering these contract strategies as options rather than as standard, as other contracts do, the *Client* can decide the individual risks and complexities of the contract and what secondary Options are required for a particular contract.

3.5.1 Contract Data by the *Client*

	Column A Question	Column B Assistance	Column C Contract Data item
10	Does the *Client* want to take the risk for inflation? YES Choose Option X1 NO Do nothing	**Discussion** Without Option X1, the contract is a firm price and the *Contractor* takes the risk for inflationary increases in the costs of labour, plant and materials (for main Options A, B, C and D only). This would generally be applicable for a contract longer than approximately 1 year and/or during periods of high inflation. **Action** Choose Option X1 if the *Client* wants to accept the risk for inflationary changes. Note that this Option cannot be used with main Options E and F.	See Contract Data entries for Option X1 in Section 3.7 of this book.
11	Does the *Client* want to accept the risk of changes in the law? YES Choose Option X2 NO Do nothing	**Discussion** Where changes in the law that take place after the Contract Date affect the *Contractor's* costs, this would generally be the *Contractor's* risk. For longer contracts where the *Contractor* might not have had warning of changes, the *Client* may choose to adopt this risk. **Action** Choose Option X2 to add a compensation event to the contract for changes to the law if the *Client* is willing to take the risk of changes to the law that affect the *Contractor's* costs.	There are no Contract Data entries for Option X2.
12	Where payment is made to the *Contractor* in more than one currency, does the *Client* carry the risk of the *exchange rate*? YES Choose Option X3 NO Do nothing	**Discussion** The effect of this Option is that the *Contractor* is protected from fluctuations in currency exchange rates where they are paid in foreign currencies for parts of the *works*. **Action** For Options A and B only, where the *Client* wishes to take the risk of *exchange rates*, choose Option X3. Provision is made for multiple currencies within Options C, D, E and F, and therefore Option X3 should not be used with Options C, D, E and F.	See Contract Data entries for Option X3 in Section 3.7 of this book
13	Do you want an ultimate holding company guarantee from the *Contractor*? YES Choose Option X4 NO Do nothing	**Discussion** An ultimate holding company guarantee is used for a similar purpose to the performance bond, except that usually physical resources, such as labour, are provided rather than solely financial resources. In addition, an ultimate holding company guarantee can only be provided if the *Contractor* has a parent company or has more than one holding company. If you want this kind of guarantee, either a performance bond or a parent company guarantee should be chosen rather than both.	There are no Contract Data entries for Option X4

	Column A Question	Column B Assistance	Column C Contract Data item
		Action If you want an ultimate holding company guarantee rather than a performance bond, choose Option X4 and include the format of the bond in the Scope.	
14	Do you want to take over parts of the *works* as they are completed? YES Choose Option X5 NO Do nothing	**Discussion** Sectional completion should be chosen if you want parts of the *works* to be completed before the whole of the *works*, where the parts of the *works* are key milestone dates leading up to Completion of the whole of the *works*. Sectional completion facilitates delay damages for key dates. The *Client* must take over those parts of the *works* that have been completed, however, so unless you want to take over each *section* of the *works* as it is completed, there is no point in choosing sectional completion just because you can deduct delay damages if the *Contractor* is late in completing that section. **Action** If you want sectional completion – that is, if you want to take over *sections* of the *works* as they are completed – choose Option X5.	See Contract Data entries for Option X5 in Section 3.7 of this book.
15	Will early Completion benefit the *Client*? YES Choose Option X6 NO Do nothing	**Discussion** Option X6 can be used to motivate the *Contractor* to achieve early Completion by providing the *Contractor* with an early Completion bonus payment. This can be used where such early Completion would benefit the *Client*, e.g. opening of a retail outlet earlier where Completion = early income from the outlet. Some *Clients* may use the potential income from an earlier opening date to calculate the bonus per day for early Completion. **Action** Where early Completion would benefit the *Client*, choose Option X6.	See Contract Data entries for Option X6 in Section 3.7 of this book.
16	Will late Completion disadvantage the *Client*? YES Choose Option X7 NO Do nothing	**Discussion** Option X7 allows for liquidated damages to be paid by the *Contractor* if they fail to complete the *works* by the Completion Date. The amount of delay damages should be a currency amount per day, e.g. pounds sterling rather than a percentage of the contract value, because the delay damages have to be a genuine pre-estimate of the loss suffered as a result of the late Completion. If delay damages are not chosen, the *Client* still has the option of suing for damages at large. **Action** Choose Option X7 if you want to include for liquidated damages where the *Contractor* achieves Completion later than the Completion Date.	See Contract Data entries for Option X7 in Section 3.7 of this book.
17	Does the *Client* require the *Contractor* to give undertakings to Others or arrange for a Subcontractor to give undertakings to Others, or to arrange for a	**Discussion** If the *Client* wants the *Contractor* or a Subcontractor to undertake to do something or not do something with regards to Others to the *Client*, then they must describe these undertakings in the Scope and must prepare them for signature. The undertakings must be described in	See Contract Data entries for X8 in Section 3.7 of this book.

	Column A Question	Column B Assistance	Column C Contract Data item
	Subcontractor to give undertakings to the *Client*? YES Choose Option X8 NO Do nothing	Contract Data part one. The ECC Guidance Notes provide that this Option facilitates a contractual link between organisations that do not otherwise have a contract with each other: i.e. the *Contractor* and Others; the Subcontractor and the *Client*; the Subcontractor and Others. The ECC Guidance Notes state that this Option provides for collateral warranties in the UK. **Action** Choose Option X8 if you want the *Contractor* to provide or arrange for the Subcontractor to provide undertakings, e.g. collateral warranties.	
18	Does the *Client* want the rights to any material provided by the *Contractor* and the Subcontractor for the design of the *works*? YES Choose Option X9 NO Do nothing	**Discussion** Option X9 requires that the *Contractor* provides to the *Client* the documents that transfer the rights to material prepared for the design of the *works* (and other rights stated in the Scope) by the *Contractor* or a Subcontractor. Where a *Contractor* is required to design a part of the *works*, it makes sense that the *Client*, who is paying for the design, then owns the design. **Action** If the *Client* wants to ■ own the *Contractor's* rights over material prepared for the design of the *works* ■ have other rights as stated in the Scope ■ own equivalent rights for material prepared by a Subcontractor ■ possess the documents that prove the transfer of rights then Option X9 should be chosen as part of the contract strategy.	There are no Contract Data entries for Option X9
19	Does the *Client* want the *Contractor* to contribute to and plan the execution of an Information Model? YES Choose Option X10 NO Do nothing	**Discussion** If the *Client* wants ■ the *Contractor* to provide an Information Execution Plan either with their tender or after the start of the contract ■ the Information Model to be delivered as part of the contract and in accordance with the Information Execution Plan ■ possibly in conjunction with other contributors ■ and for it all to be time-lined and project managed then the *Client* should choose Option X10 as part of the contract strategy. **Action** Choose Option X10 if you want the *Contractor* to prepare for and contribute to an Information Model.	See Contract Data entries for X10 in Section 3.7 of this book.
20	Does the *Client* want to be able to terminate for a reason not included in the Termination Table? YES Choose Option X11 NO Do nothing	**Discussion** Some *Clients* for some projects want the ability to be able to terminate the contract for any reason, i.e. a reason not included in the Termination Table in clause 90.2. Option X11 includes the procedures on termination and the amounts due to the *Contractor* on termination. **Action** Choose Option X11 if you want to be able to terminate the contract for any reason.	There are no Contract Data entries for Option X11

	Column A Question	Column B Assistance	Column C Contract Data item
21	Does the *Client* wish to include for multiparty collaboration? YES Choose Option X12 NO Do nothing	**Discussion** This Option allows for managing the contract as if it were a partnership (does not create a legal partnership). The organisations that are a part of the partnership are stated by the *Client*, and Partnering Information about how the partnership is to be managed is listed in the Scope. Option X12 includes for Key Performance Indicators and so cannot be used with Option X20. **Action** If the *Client* wishes to include for multiparty collaboration, Option X12 should be chosen.	See Contract Data entries for X12 in Section 3.7 of this book.
22	Do you want a performance bond from the *Contractor*? YES Choose Option X13 NO Do nothing	**Discussion** A performance bond provides a backup resource if the *Contractor* fails to complete the contract **Action** If you want a performance bond, choose Option X13, and include the format of the bond into the Scope.	See Contract Data entries for Option X13 in Section 3.7 of this book.
23	Does the project involve a substantial capital outlay by the *Contractor* and is the *Client* willing to finance it? YES Choose Option X14 NO Do nothing	**Discussion** If a large item of Equipment is required to be purchased before the work starts, the *Client* may choose to make an advance payment to the *Contractor* to assist their cash flow. The *Client* may also require a bond from the *Contractor*, which, of course, will cost the *Contractor* to obtain. **Action** If you want to advance the *Contractor* payments, then choose Option X14. If a bond is required, then include the format of the bond in the Scope. An alternative to choosing Option X14 is to include an item in the *activity schedule* or *bill of quantities* for the purchase of the item.	See Contract Data entries for Option X14 in Section 3.7 of this book.
24	Is the *Contractor* required to design part of or the whole of the *works*? YES Choose Option X15 NO Do nothing	**Discussion** The standard for the *Contractor's* design liability is fitness for purpose. It is often difficult for a designer to insure for more than reasonable skill and care. Option X15 reduces the design liability to that of reasonable skill and care. It should be remembered that even with reasonable skill and care there is still a requirement for the design to be fit for its purpose, e.g. a contractor-designed warehouse floor should be suitable for fork-lift trucks to run over them. **Action** Choose Option X15 to reduce the *Contractor's* liability for Defects due to their design from fitness for purpose to reasonable skill and care.	See Contract Data entries for Option X15 in Section 3.7 of this book.
25	Does the *Client* want to retain a fund for use at the end of the contract to ensure the correction of Defects? YES Choose Option X16 NO Do nothing	**Discussion** The purpose of retention is to enable the *Client* to retain a proportion of the amount paid to the *Contractor* as security for the correction of Defects after Completion and as an additional motivation for the *Contractor* to complete the *works*. The procedure in the ECC is slightly different from traditional contracts. In traditional contracts a retention percentage, typically 2.5–5%, is withheld on each and every interim payment from the	See Contract Data entries for Option X16 in Section 3.7 of this book.

	Column A Question	Column B Assistance	Column C Contract Data item
		outset of the contract, but the ECC refers to a *retention-free amount*. The ECC Guidance Notes suggest that this could be set at, say, 70% of the contract sum, the idea being that the *retention-free amount* aids the *Contractor's* cash flow in the early part of the contract when they most need it. Once the *retention-free amount* has been reached, a higher *retention percentage* than normal is suggested. The net effect is the same except that the retention fund is built up in the latter part of the contract. **Action** If you think you will need added security at the end of the contract, then choosing Option X16 is a method of achieving this.	
26	Does the *Client* want to liquidate any damages that may be suffered in consequence of low-performance or substandard work? YES Choose Option X17 NO Do nothing	**Discussion** Where work is of a low standard or substandard, and the standard is clearly stated in the Scope, the *Client* may choose to include in the contract liquidated damages that represent the damage they would suffer in consequence of the substandard work. Other options are to insist that the *Contractor* achieves the standard stated in the Scope, to have someone else correct the Defect and charge the costs to the *Contractor*, or accept the Defect and a quotation from the *Contractor* for reduced Prices. This may be particularly relevant on process-plant-type projects, e.g. a gas desulphurisation plant at a power station is required by the Scope to remove 95% of the sulphur from the gases omitted from the flues but the plant only achieves 90%. **Action** Choose Option X17 if you wish to liquidate the damages suffered in consequence of the *Contractor* producing low-performance/substandard work.	See Contract Data entries for Option X17 in Section 3.7 of this book.
27	Does the *Client* wish to limit the *Contractor's* liability under the contract for loss, damage to property or design for a specified period of time? YES Choose Option X18 NO Do nothing	**Discussion** Option X18 limits the liability of the *Contractor* to the *Client* for indirect or consequential loss, loss or damage to the *Client's* property, latent defects under design and total liability. Although not specifically allowed for, it may be that these different limitations can be stated individually or included as 'unlimited'. **Action** Choose Option X18 to limit the *Contractor's* liability.	See Contract Data entries for Option X18 in Section 3.7 of this book.
28	Does the *Client* wish to include Key Performance Indicators? YES Choose Option X20 NO Do nothing	**Discussion** Option X20 facilitates the inclusion of an Incentive Schedule, which details the targets for Key Performance Indicators. Amounts of money are included in the Incentive Schedule. The *Contractor* is required to report on their performance against each of the Key Performance Indicators to the *Project Manager*. **Action** Choose Option X20 to include Key Performance Indicators, targets and monetary incentives for the *Contractor*.	See Contract Data entries for Option X20 in Section 3.7 of this book.

	Column A Question	Column B Assistance	Column C Contract Data item
29	Does the *Client* want to allow the *Contractor* to propose a Scope change to reduce the cost of operating and maintaining an asset? YES Choose Option X21 NO Do nothing	**Discussion** Although there is no reason why the *Contractor* could not propose changes to the Scope in any case, Option X21 specifically allows for the *Contractor* to propose to the *Project Manager* that the Scope is changed in order to reduce the cost of operating and maintaining an asset. The procedure details the *Project Manager* considering a quotation from the *Contractor*. **Action** Choose Option X21 if you want to facilitate the *Contractor's* proposing a change to the Scope in order to reduce the cost of operating and maintaining an asset.	There are no Contract Data entries for Option X21
30	For Option C and E contracts, does the *Client* want early *Contractor* involvement, with two stages to the project and procedures describing the move from Stage One to Stage Two? YES Choose Option X22 NO Do nothing	**Discussion** Option X22 facilitates the *Client* describing a Budget and Stages One and Two, with procedures for receiving forecasts of the Defined Cost of the work to be done in Stage One and the Project Cost. The *Contractor* also submits design proposals and prices for Stage Two, with forecasts of the effect of the design proposal on the Project Cost and the Accepted Programme. The *Client* can remove Stage Two from the Scope. Incentives are included for a final Project Cost less than the Budget. **Action** Choose Option X22 if you want to have early *Contractor* involvement.	See Contract Data entries for Option X22 in Section 3.7 of this book.
31	Does the *Client* want the *Contractor* to establish a Project Bank Account and include Named Suppliers in the contract for the operation of the Project Bank Account and Trust Deed with procedures for making payment? YES Choose Option Y(UK)1 NO Do nothing	**Discussion** The *Contractor* sets up the Project Bank Account and includes Named Suppliers in the contract for the operation of the Project Bank Account and Trust Deed. The *Client* makes payment into the Project Bank Account of the amount due to be paid under the contract and payments are made from the Project Bank Account to the *Contractor* and their Subcontractors and Named Suppliers. **Action** Choose Option Y(UK)1 if you want to pay the *Contractor* through a Project Bank Account and have the *Contractor* pay their Subcontractors and Named Suppliers in the same way.	See Contract Data entries for Option Y(UK)1 in Section 3.7 of this book.
32	If the contract is a construction contract in accordance with the HGCR Act, does the *Client* wish to include the required statements **relating to the period for payment** in the contract? YES Choose Option Y(UK)2 NO Do nothing (and the Scheme for Construction Contracts will apply)	**Discussion** Option Y(UK)2 relates only to payment. If the contract is a construction contract in accordance with the Act and Option Y(UK)2 is not chosen, then the Scheme for Construction Contracts will be read into the contract. The *Client* should consider their position in the light of the clauses in both Y(UK)2 and the Scheme and make their decision. **Action** Choose Option Y(UK)2 if the *Client* thinks that the contract is a construction contract in accordance with the HGCR Act and they do not want the Scheme to apply.	The Contract Data entries relating to Option Y(UK)2 are specific to Contract Data section 5 (payment) and therefore appear in Contract Data section 5 (payment) in Section 3.7 of this book.

	Column A Question	Column B Assistance	Column C Contract Data item
33	Does the *Client* wish to take into account the Contracts (Rights of Third Parties) Act 1999? (UK only) YES Choose Option Y(UK)3 NO Do nothing	**Discussion** Option Y(UK)3 covers the introduction of the Contracts (Rights of Third Parties) Act 1999 for use with the ECC when used in England and Wales. This law is covered by common law within Scotland, and is therefore not required for contracts for which the *law of the contract* is the law of Scotland. The optional clause should be included in all contracts that came into existence on or after 11 May 2000. **Action** If the *Client* wants to take the HGCR Act into account, they should choose Option Y(UK)3.	See Contract Data entries for Option Y(UK)3 in Section 3.7 of this book.
34	Does the *Client* wish to add their own conditions of contract? YES Choose Option Z NO Do nothing	**Discussion** Most *Clients* would prefer to include some of their own conditions of contract, such as confidentiality. In general, however, additional conditions should only be used when absolutely necessary to accommodate special needs. The *additional conditions of contract* should be drafted in the same style as the core and optional clauses, using the same defined terms and other terminology. They should be carefully checked for consistency with the other conditions. **Action** Choose Option Z if the *Client* wants to include for *additional conditions of contract* that take into account special circumstances for the particular project.	See Contract Data entries for Option Z in Section 3.7 of this book.

3.5.2 Contract Data provided by the *Contractor – Client* choices

Note: Only three secondary Options require the *Client* to make a choice in the Contract Data by the *Contractor*.

	Column A Question	Column B Assistance	Column C Contract Data item
35	Has Option X10 been chosen by the *Client*? YES Choose whether to include the relevant statement in CD1 or CD2 NO Remove the statements from both CD1 and CD2	**Discussion** If Option X10 has been chosen by the *Client*, then the *Contractor* may be required to include an Information Execution Plan with their tender. If the *Client* has included the Option X10 statement in Contract Data part two and not Contract Data part one, then the *Contractor* will need to provide the Information Execution Plan with their tender. **Action** The *Client* should include the relevant secondary Option statement in Contract Data part two for the tenderers to complete as part of their tender. In their tender, the *Contractor* should ■ indicate in Contract Data part two where the *Client* can find the Information Execution Plan in the tender ■ make sure to include the Information Execution Plan as part of their tender.	**Contract Data part two** ■ The *information execution plan* identified in the Contract Data is ....

	Column A Question	Column B Assistance	Column C Contract Data item
36	Has Option X22 been chosen by the *Client*? YES Include the statements in CD2 NO Remove the statements from CD2	**Discussion** For early *Contractor* involvement, the *Contractor* is required to include information in their tendered Contract Data part two about the *key persons* who will be involved in Stage One (most likely designers) and information that describes how the *Contractor* will prepare their assessment of the Prices for Stage Two. **Action** The *Client* should include the relevant secondary Option statement in Contract Data part two for the tenderers to complete as part of their tender. In their tender, the *Contractor* should ■ provide information in Contract Data part two about the names and other details of the people who will be involved in Stage One ■ provide information about where the *Client* can find the Pricing Information in the tender ■ make sure to include information about how they will provide their assessment of the Prices for Stage Two as part of their tender.	**Contract Data part two** ■ The Stage One *key persons* are Name (1) .... Job .... Responsibilities .... Qualifications .... Experience .... Name (2) .... Job .... Responsibilities .... Qualifications .... Experience .... ■ The Pricing Information is in ....
37	Has Option Y(UK)1 been chosen by the *Client*? YES Include the statements in CD2 NO Remove the statements from CD2	**Discussion** The *Contractor* sets up the Project Bank Account and includes Named Suppliers in the contract for the operation of the Project Bank Account and Trust Deed. The *Contractor* is required to provide details about the Project Bank Account in their tender and to provide the names of the suppliers who will be included in the Project Bank Account. **Action** The *Client* should include the relevant secondary Option statements in Contract Data part two for the tenderers to complete as part of their tender. In their tender, the *Contractor* should ■ provide information in Contract Data part two about the *project bank* ■ list the *named suppliers*.	■ The *project bank* is .... ■ *named suppliers* are ......

3.6. Part 4 of this chapter: choosing optional Contract Data statements

This part of the chapter continues with questions about your chosen contract strategy, guiding you in choices about the optional statements that appear in the Contract Data as if-statements in the nine sections of core clauses. These optional statements represent aspects of the *Client's* contract strategy (the *Contractor's* in the Engineering and Construction Subcontract), and should be decided before issuing tender documentation.

If the *Client* does not wish to include the optional statement, then both the if-statement in the Contract Data and the optional statement should be removed from the Contract Data. If the *Client* wishes to include the optional statement in the Contract Data, then the if-statement should still be removed from the Contract Data, but the optional statement should be completed by the *Client* and included in the Contract Data.

Where there is a choice to include a statement in CD1 or CD2, then the *Client* should delete the if-statement and the optional statement from the part of the Contract Data to which the optional statement does not apply, and then delete the if-statement but include the optional statement in the Contract Data to which the optional statement does apply. If the optional statement is included in CD1, then the *Client* should complete the statement. If the optional statement is included in CD2, then the *Client* should leave the optional statement blank, as it appears in the ECC published document.

There are only two of these statements, one referring to when the *Client* wants to receive the first programme and the other referring to who determines the *completion date* – the *Contractor* or the *Client*.

Any reference to CD1 is a reference to Contract Data part one by the *Client*. Any reference to CD2 is a reference to Contract Data part two by the *Contractor*.

3.6.1 Contract Data by the *Client*
3.6.1.1 Contract Data by the *Client*: section 1, 'General'

There are no optional Contract Data statements in section 1, 'General', of Contract Data part one.

3.6.1.2 Contract Data by the *Client*: section 2, 'The *Contractor's* main responsibilities'

	Column A Question	Column B Assistance	Column C Contract Data item
38	Does the *Client* want some work to be completed by *key dates*? YES Choose the optional statement in CD1 NO Delete the if-statement and the optional statement from CD1	**Discussion** The *Client* may decide to include a date or a series of dates that represent the dates by which the *Contractor* is to meet the *condition* described in the Contract Data. **Action** If the *Client* has identified work to be completed by *key dates*, then this should be incorporated into the Contract Data. Note that the condition of work described needs to be very clearly defined.	**Contract Data part one** ■ The *key dates* and *conditions* to be met are *condition* to be met *key date* (1) .... (2) .... (3) ....
39	Has the *Client* chosen main Option C, D, E or F? YES The optional statement should be chosen and completed in the Contract Data NO delete the if-statement and the optional statement from CD1	**Discussion** For all main Options except Options A and B, the *Contractor* is required to provide regular forecasts of the total Defined Cost so that the *Project Manager* is kept up to date about the cost of the project as it progresses, as it cannot be easily measured against an *activity schedule* or *bill of quantities* as it can be in Options A and B, respectively. **Action** If the *Client* has chosen any of main Options C, D, E or F, they should include this optional statement in the Contract Data.	**Contract Data part one** ■ The *Contractor* prepares forecasts of the total Defined Cost for the whole of the *works* at intervals no longer than ....

3.6.1.3 Contract Data by the *Client*: section 3, 'Time'

	Column A Question	Column B Assistance	Column C Contract Data item
40	Does the *Client* want the *Contractor* to decide the *completion date*? YES Choose the optional statement in CD2 (see item 56 below) NO Choose the optional statement in CD1	**Discussion** The ECC allows for either the *Contractor* or the *Client* to decide the *completion date*. In general, where the *Client* wishes the *Contractor* to tender their programme (see the next question) and therefore also tender their realistic *completion date*, the *Client* would not dictate the *completion date* but would allow the *Contractor* to provide it with their tender. In most instances, however, the *Client* has a programme of work and a requirement for the *Contractor* to finish by a specific date. **Action** If the *Client* wants the *Contractor* to decide the *completion date* for the whole of the *works*: ■ delete the optional statement in Contract Data part one ■ include the optional statement in Contract Data part two (and leave blank). If the *Client* wants to dictate the *completion date* for the whole of the *works*: ■ delete the optional statement in Contract Data part two ■ include the optional statement in Contract Data part one section 3, and complete the bullet point by adding the date of completion.	**Contract Data part one** ■ The *completion date* for the whole of the *works* is .... **Contract Data part two** ■ The *completion date* for the whole of the *works* is ....
41	Does the *Client* want to see a programme with the tender? YES Choose the optional statement in CD2 (see item 55 below) NO Choose the optional statement in CD1	**Discussion** The *Client* may receive a first programme from the *Contractor* either at the tender stage or after the Contract Date. Where the *Client* wishes to ensure that the *Contractor* is able to adhere to dictated dates, or where the *Client* wishes the *Contractor* to dictate their own programme, then the *Client* would normally choose to see a programme with the tender. Whichever programme is chosen, it will become the Accepted Programme after it has been accepted by the *Project Manager*. There should therefore be very little difference between the 'tender programme' and the 'contract programme'. **Action** If the *Client* wants a programme with the tender: ■ delete the optional statement in Contract Data part one ■ include the optional statement in Contract Data part two (and leave blank) if the *Client* only wants a programme after the Contract Date: ■ delete the optional statement in Contract Data part two ■ include the optional statement in Contract Data part one section 3 and complete the bullet point by adding the number of days or weeks after the Contract Date by which time the *Client* wants to see the programme.	**Contract Data part two** ■ The programme identified in the Contract Data is .... **Contract Data part one** ■ The period after the Contract Date within which the *Contractor* is to submit a first programme for acceptance is ....

	Column A Question	Column B Assistance	Column C Contract Data item
42	Is the *Client* willing to take over the *works* if the *Contractor* completes the *works* before the Completion Date? YES Do nothing NO Choose the optional statement in CD1	**Discussion** Sometimes, if a *Contractor* completes early, the *Client* might not be willing to take over the *works*, e.g. due to constraints on the interaction between the *works* and the rest of the project. If this is the case, then the *Client* needs to make this clear, since the default position is that the *Client* takes over the *works* within 2 weeks after Completion. **Action** If the *Client* is unwilling to take over the *works* if Completion is before the Completion Date, then include the optional statement in Contract Data part one section 3.	**Contract Data part one** ■ The *Client* **is/is not** willing to take over the *works* before the Completion Date

3.6.1.4 Contract Data by the *Client*: section 4, 'Quality management'

There are no optional Contract Data statements in section 4, 'Quality management', of Contract Data part one.

3.6.1.5 Contract Data by the *Client*: section 5, 'Payment'

	Column A Question	Column B Assistance	Column C Contract Data item
43a	For contracts where Option Y(UK)2 has not been chosen: clause 51.2 requires the *Client* to make payment within 3 weeks after the assessment. Is this time sufficient? YES Do nothing NO Choose the optional statement in CD1	**Discussion** The trigger for payment is the assessment date, not the payment certificate or the receipt of invoice. Since the payment certificate is given to the *Contractor* 1 week after the assessment date, and any invoice requested a number of days after the payment certificate, this reduces the time allowed for the accounts department to make a payment. If payment is made 4 weeks after the assessment day, and assuming the invoice is received on time, then the accounts department has 2 weeks from receipt of the invoice to make a payment. **Action** If the *Client* wants to increase the period for payment, then include the optional statement in Contract Data part one section 5.	**Contract Data part one** ■ The period within which payments are made is ....
43b	For Option Y(UK)2 contracts only: the *Client* is obliged to make payment within 14 days after the date on which the payment becomes due. Is this time sufficient? YES Do nothing NO Choose the optional statement in CD1 (taken from Y(UK)2)	**Discussion** The trigger for payment is the date on which payment becomes due. This date is 7 days after the assessment date. The default in Option Y(UK)2 is that the *Client* has 14 days after the date when payment becomes due to make a payment. This is the same amount of time as clause 51.2 gives the *Client* to pay. If the *Client* considers this time period to be too short, then they may insert a longer time period in Contract Data part one. **Action** If the *Client* has chosen Option Y(UK)2 and wants to increase the period for payment, then include in Contract Data part one section 5 the optional statement that appears near the end of Contract Data part one in the ECC pro forma.	**Contract Data part one** ■ The period for payment is ...... days after the date on which payment became due

Note that optional statements 43a and 43b are chosen in the alternative.

	Column A Question	Column B Assistance	Column C Contract Data item
44a 44b	Has the *Client* chosen main Option C, D, E or F? YES The optional statement should be chosen and completed in the Contract Data NO delete the if-statement and the optional statement from CD1	**Discussion** All main Options except A and B require the use of *exchange rates* for payments not made in the *currency of the contract* (Option C/D clause 50.7 and Option E/F clause 50.8). **Action** If the *Client* has chosen any of main Options C, D, E or F, it should include this optional statement in the Contract Data.	**Contract Data part one** ■ The *exchange rates* are those published in . . . . on . . . . (date)

3.6.1.6 Contract Data by the *Client*: section 6, 'Compensation events'

	Column A Question	Column B Assistance	Column C Contract Data item
45	Does the *Client* have access to recorded *weather data* to be provided in the Contract Data? YES Do nothing (see entries 87–90a in Section 3.7.1) NO Choose the optional statement in CD1	**Discussion** Clause 60.1(13) requires a comparison of recorded *weather measurements* against historical *weather data*. If there are no historical *weather data* that the *Client* can provide, the *Client* should provide assumed *weather data* using the optional clause in the Contract Data. **Action** If there are no historical recorded *weather data*, then the *Client* should use and populate the optional statement referring to *weather data* in Contract Data part one.	**Contract Data part one** ■ Assumed values for the 10-year weather return *weather data* for each *weather measurement* for each calendar month are . . . .
46	Has the *Client* chosen main Option A or B? YES Choose and complete the optional statement in CD1 NO Delete the if-statement and the optional statement from CD1	**Discussion** If a change to the Scope proposed by the *Contractor* and accepted by the *Project Manager* results in a compensation event for which the *Contractor's* quotation reduces the total Defined Cost, then the reduction to the Prices is only half of the reduction in the quotation, or a different percentage stated in the Contract Data. **Action** If the *Client* has chosen main Option A or B, then include the statement about the *value engineering percentage* in Contract Data part one.	**Contract Data part one** ■ The *value engineering percentage* is 50%, unless another percentage is stated here, in which case it is . . . . .%
47	Has the *Client* chosen main Option B or D? YES Choose and complete the optional statement in CD1 NO Delete the if-statement and the optional statement from CD1	**Discussion** If the *Client* has chosen main Option B or D, then the *Client* has to state the *method of measurement* to be used in clause 60.6. **Action** If the *Client* has chosen main Option B or D, then include the statement about the *method of measurement* in Contract Data part one.	**Contract Data part one** ■ The *method of measurement* is . . . .
48	Does the *Client* want to include additional compensation events? YES Choose the optional statement in CD1 NO Delete the if-statement and the optional statement from CD1	**Discussion** The *Client* has the option of including additional compensation events to be applied during the project, and these should be stated in the Contract Data. **Action** If the *Client* wants additional compensation events to apply, then choose the optional statement in Contract Data part one.	**Contract Data part one** ■ These are additional compensation events . . . .

3.6.1.7 Contract Data by the *Client*: section 7, 'Title'

There are no optional Contract Data statements in section 7, 'Title', of Contract Data part one.

3.6.1.8 Contract Data by the *Client*: section 8, 'Liabilities and insurance'

	Column A Question	Column B Assistance	Column C Contract Data item
49	Are there additional *Client* liabilities to be included in the contract? YES Choose the optional statement in CD1 NO Delete the if-statement and the optional statement from CD1	**Discussion** Clause 80.1 of the *conditions of contract* allows additional *Client* liabilities to be stated in the Contract Data. The *Client* should use this when they wish to limit the *Contractor's* risk for specific items of risk that the *Client* is better able to control. **Action** If the *Client* intends to adopt extra liabilities, choose the optional statement in Contract Data part one and include it in Contract Data part one section 8.	**Contract Data part one** ■ These are additional *Client's* liabilities (1) .... (2) .... (3) ....
50	Does the *Client* provide Plant and Materials to the *Contractor*? YES Choose the optional statement in CD1 NO Delete the if-statement and the optional statement from CD1	**Discussion** If the *Client* free issues to the *Contractor* certain items of Plant and Materials, the *Client* might want the *Contractor* to insure for this free-issue material. In such a case, this optional statement would be chosen, with the amount of insurance decided by the *Client*. **Action** If the *Client* free issues Plant and Materials to the *Contractor*, and the *Client* wants the *Contractor* to insure for those items, then the optional statement in Contract Data part one should be chosen and included in Contract Data part one section 8.	**Contract Data part one** ■ The insurance against loss of or damage to the *works*, Plant and Materials is to include cover for Plant and Materials provided by the *Client* for an amount of ....
51	Is the *Client* intending to provide any of the insurances in the insurance table? YES Choose the optional statement in CD1 NO Delete the if-statement and the optional statement from CD1	**Discussion** Where the Insurance Table in clause 83.3 of the *conditions of contract* does not represent the way the *Client* wishes to insure, this optional statement and the next are the mechanism for changing the table. In particular, *Clients* sometimes self-insure, or provide the insurance for the *works* themselves. **Action** If the *Client* provides some of the insurances in the insurance table, choose the optional statement in Contract Data part one and include it in section 8.	**Contract Data part one** ■ The *Client* provides these insurances from the Insurance Table: (1) Insurance against .... Minimum amount of cover is .... The deductibles are .... (2) Insurance against .... Minimum amount of cover is .... The deductibles are ....
52	Is the *Client* intending to provide additional insurances? YES Choose the optional statement in CD1 NO Delete the if-statement and the optional statement from CD1	**Discussion** Where the Insurance Table in clause 83.32 of the *conditions of contract* does not represent the way the *Client* wishes to insure, this optional statement and the previous one are the mechanism for changing the table. **Action** If the *Client* intends to provide additional insurances to those already stated in the Insurance Table, then this optional statement should be chosen and included in section 8 of Contract Data part one.	**Contract Data part one** ■ The *Client* provides these additional insurances (1) Insurance against .... Minimum amount of cover is .... The deductibles are .... (2) Insurance against .... Minimum amount of cover is .... The deductibles are ....

	Column A Question	Column B Assistance	Column C Contract Data item
53	Does the *Client* require the *Contractor* to provide additional insurances? YES Choose the optional statement in CD1 NO Delete the if-statement and the optional statement from CD1	**Discussion** The *Client* could want the *Contractor* to provide additional insurances; for example, if design is a part of the *Contractor's* scope of work, then the *Client* is likely to want the *Contractor* to provide professional indemnity insurance. **Action** If the *Client* wants the *Contractor* to provide additional insurances, then the optional statement in Contract Data part one should be chosen and included in section 8 and the required insurance indicated.	**Contract Data part one** ■ The *Contractor* provides these additional insurances (1) Insurance against .... Minimum amount of cover is .... The deductibles are .... (2) Insurance against .... Minimum amount of cover is .... The deductibles are ....

3.6.1.9 Contract Data by the *Client*: section 9, 'Termination'

There are no optional Contract Data statements in section 9, 'Termination', of Contract Data part one.

3.6.2 Contract Data provided by the *Contractor* – the *Client's* choices
3.6.2.1 Contract Data by the *Contractor*: section 1, 'General'

There are no optional Contract Data statements in section 1, 'General', of Contract Data part two.

3.6.2.2 Contract Data by the *Contractor*: section 2, 'The *Contractor's* main responsibilities'

	Column A Question for the *Client*	Column B Assistance	Column C Contract Data item
54	Is the *Contractor* required to design part of or the whole of the *works*? YES Choose the optional statement in CD2 NO Do nothing	**Discussion** If the *Contractor* is required to design a part of the *works*, then the *Client* is likely to want to see the *Contractor's* design proposal at the tender stage. The tenderer would therefore be required to include the proposal in their tender. **Action** If the *Client* wants to see the *Contractor's* design proposal at tender stage, the optional statement in Contract Data part two should be chosen.	**Contract Data part two** ■ The Scope provided by the *Contractor* for its design is in ....

3.6.2.3 Contract Data by the *Contractor*: section 3, 'Time'

	Column A Question	Column B Assistance	Column C Contract Data item
55	Does the *Client* want to see a programme with the tender? YES Choose the optional statement in CD2 NO Choose the optional statement in CD1 (see item 41 above)	**Discussion** The *Client* may receive a first programme from the *Contractor* either at the tender stage or after the Contract Date. Where the *Client* wishes to ensure that the *Contractor* is able to adhere to dictated dates, or where the *Client* wishes the *Contractor* to dictate their own programme, then the *Client* would normally choose to see a programme with the tender. Whichever programme is chosen, it will become the Accepted Programme after it has been accepted by the *Project Manager*. There should therefore be very little difference between the 'tender programme' and the 'contract programme'. **Action** If the *Client* wants a programme with the tender: ■ delete the if-statement and optional statement in Contract Data part one ■ include the optional statement in Contract Data part two (and leave blank). If the *Client* only wants a programme after the Contract Date: ■ delete the if-statement and optional statement in Contract Data part two ■ include the optional statement in Contract Data part one section 3 and complete the bullet point by adding the number of days or weeks after the Contract Date by which time the *Client* wants to see the programme.	**Contract Data part two** The programme identified in the Contract Data is .... **Contract Data part one** ■ The period after the Contract Date within which the *Contractor* is to submit a first programme for acceptance is ....
56	Does the *Client* want the *Contractor* to decide the *completion date*? YES Choose the optional statement in CD2 NO Choose the optional statement in CD1 (see item 40 above)	**Discussion** The ECC allows for either the *Contractor* or the *Client* to decide the *completion date*. In general, where the *Client* wishes the *Contractor* to tender their programme (see the previous question) and therefore also tender their realistic *completion date*, the *Client* would not dictate the *completion date*, but would allow the *Contractor* to provide it with their tender. In most instances, however, the *Client* has a programme of work and a requirement for the *Contractor* to finish by a specific date. **Action** If the *Client* wants the *Contractor* to decide the *completion date* for the whole of the *works*: ■ delete the if-statement and optional statement in Contract Data part one ■ include the optional statement in Contract Data part two (and leave blank). If the *Client* wants to dictate the *completion date* for the whole of the *works*: ■ delete the if-statement and optional statement in Contract Data part two and include the optional statement in Contract Data part one section 3 and complete the bullet point by adding the date of completion.	**Contract Data part one** ■ The *completion date* for the whole of the *works* is ...... **Contract Data part two** ■ The *completion date* for the whole of the *works* is ......

3.6.2.4 Contract Data by the *Contractor*: section 4, 'Quality management'

There are no optional Contract Data statements in section 4, 'Quality management', of Contract Data part two.

3.6.2.5 Contract Data by the *Contractor*: section 5, 'Payment'

	Column A Question for the *Client*	Column B Assistance	Column C Contract Data item
57	Which main Options has the *Client* chosen? (See questions 1 and 2 above.) The statements to include in section 5 of the Contract Data depend on whether Option A, B, C, D, E or F was chosen.	**Discussion** Each of the main Options describes a different approach to payment, and so the statements included in Contract Data part two differ depending on the main Option chosen. **Action** Include these two statements in Contract Data part two and leave blank if main Option A was chosen. **Action** Include these two statements in Contract Data part two and leave blank if main Option B was chosen. **Action** Include these two statements in Contract Data part two and leave blank if main Option C was chosen. **Action** Include these two statements in Contract Data part two and leave blank if main Option D was chosen. **Action** There are no statements required in Contract Data part two if main Option E was chosen. **Action** Include this statement in Contract Data part two and leave blank if main Option F was chosen.	**Contract Data part two** ■ The *activity schedule* is .... ■ The tendered total of the Prices is .... **Contract Data part two** ■ The *bill of quantities* is .... ■ The tendered total of the Prices is .... **Contract Data part two** ■ The *activity schedule* is .... ■ The tendered total of the Prices is .... **Contract Data part two** ■ The *bill of quantities* is .... ■ The tendered total of the Prices is .... ■ Work which the *Contractor* will do is activity *price* ....

3.6.2.6 Contract Data by the *Contractor*: section 6, 'Compensation events'

There are no optional Contract Data statements in section 6, 'Compensation events', of Contract Data part two.

3.6.2.7 Contract Data by the *Contractor*: section 7, 'Title'

There are no optional Contract Data statements in section 7, 'Title', of Contract Data part two.

3.6.2.8 Contract Data by the *Contractor*: section 8, 'Liabilities and insurance'

There are no optional Contract Data statements in section 8, 'Liabilities and insurance', of Contract Data part two.

3.6.2.9 Contract Data by the *Contractor*: section 9, 'Termination'

There are no optional Contract Data statements in section 9, 'Termination', of Contract Data part two.

3.7 Part 5 of this chapter: all entries in the Contract Data

This part of the table lists all the information that is needed to complete Contract Data part one by the *Client*, incorporating the optional statements detailed above.

3.7.1 Contract Data part one by the *Client*

	Statement required	Contract Data entry
1. General		
58	A list of the main Option, W Option and secondary Options chosen is required based on the choices made in Sections 3.3–3.6 of this book.	■ The *conditions of contract* are the core clauses and the following clauses for the main Option, the Option for resolving and avoiding disputes and secondary Options of the NEC4 Engineering and Construction Contract June 2017
58a	Select main Option A, B, C, D, E or F (see questions 1 and 2 above)	■ Main Option ....
58b	Select W1, W2 or W3 (see questions 3–7 above)	■ Option for resolving and avoiding disputes ....
58c	Select secondary options (see questions 10–34 above)	■ Secondary Options
59	A description of the *works* is required, including all aspects of the work that is to be done, e.g. manufacture, supply, delivery to the Site, installation, testing and commissioning.	■ The *works* are ....
60	The name and registered address of the *Client*. This is the default address for receiving information – see clause 13.2.	■ The *Client* is Name .... Address for communications .... Address for electronic communications ....
61	Name and address of the *Project Manager*. The *Project Manager* should be on Site all the time and is the person by whom most of the decisions are made that impact on the budget or the programme.	■ The *Project Manager* is Name .... Address for communications .... Address for electronic communications ....
62	Name and address of the *Supervisor*. The *Supervisor* is in charge of testing, quality and title only.	■ The *Supervisor* is Name .... Address for communications .... Address for electronic communications ....
63	The place where the Scope is to be found should be stated here. The contract places considerable importance on the Scope. By reference here in the Contract Data, the documents that contain this information are established. By definition (clause 11.2(16)), the information includes not only design but also specific requirements regarding how the *Contractor* is to administer and manage the *works*, and therefore several documents may need to be included. An example is ■ The Scope is in the document entitled 'Scope' and all documents referred to in it.	■ The Scope is in ....

	Statement required	Contract Data entry
64	The place where the Site Information is to be found should be stated here. An example is ■ The Site Information is in the document entitled 'Site Information' and all documents referred to in it.	■ The Site Information is in ....
65	The information entered here determines the limits of the Site (refer to clause 11.2(17)). This is defined separately from the *working areas* that the *Contractor* identifies in Contract Data part two. The definition of the Site is important as it relates to ■ *access dates* ■ compensations events, e.g. the *Client* fails to give access to the Site by the date shown on the Accepted Programme ■ title to objects/items within the Site ■ definition of the *Client's* risks, i.e. 'use or occupation of the Site' ■ termination – the *Client* may instruct the *Contractor* to leave the Site; a drawing showing the boundaries of the Site is the easiest way to complete this statement, e.g. – The *boundaries of the site* are as shown on drawing DR/xyz/001.	■ The *boundaries of the site* are ....
66	The language refers to the language in which communications are written (see clause 13.1).	■ The *language of this contract* is ....
67	The law of the contract would generally be the country in which the Site is situated; however, larger companies whose headquarters are situated elsewhere might prefer the law to be that of a country other than where the Site is situated.	■ The *law of the contract* is the law of .. ..

68	This determines the length of time allowed under the contract for either party to reply to a communication. A communication is not defined but generally includes the communications that the Parties acting under the contract undertake as part of the contractual requirements, e.g. instructions, certificates, submissions, proposals, acceptances, notifications and replies. It is important to note the content of clause 13.7, which states that notifications and certificates required by the contract are communicated separately from other communications. This has particular relevance to the notification of compensation events, which cannot be notified as part of another communication such as the minutes of a meeting. The contract also states specific time periods for the issue of such identified notifications.
	
	 This period of time should be tailored so that both the *Contractor* and the *Project Manager* can respond to a communication within the time period stated. If a longer period of time is required for a specific type of communication, such as drawings, then two time periods could be stated, e.g.
	
	 ■ The *period for reply* is three weeks for drawings and two weeks for all other communications.
		■ The *period for reply* is .... except that
		    – The *period for reply* for .... is ....
		    – The *period for reply* for .... is ....

69	The definition for the Early Warning Register (clause 11.2(8)) requires a list of risks to be described in the Contract Data. This list may be added to by the *Project Manager* or the *Contractor* through the early warning mechanism. The contract requires early warning meetings to be held regularly through the period of the contract (clause 15.2). The *Client* should identify what that interval is. The intention of the statement is that a period of time such as 'every 4 weeks' is provided; however there is no reason why the *Client* could not provide a more specific time such as that early warning meetings are to be held on the last Friday of every month.	■ The following matters will be included in the Early Warning Register .... ■ Early warning meetings are to be held at intervals no longer than ....

	Statement required	Contract Data entry

2. The *Contractor's* main responsibilities

| 70 | **If the *Client* has identified work which is set to meet a stated condition by a *key date***

This is an optional statement. See question 38 above. Where the *Client* needs the *Contractor* to meet a certain Condition by a Key Date, then the Condition and the Key Date (both defined in clause 11.2(11)) are described in the Contract Data, and the consequences of not meeting the Condition or Key Date are described in clause 25.3. This facility to set programme requirements is useful if the *Client* wants the *Contractor* to do things by a certain date so that, for example, follow-on work by another contractor is not delayed. | ■ The *key dates* and *conditions* to be met are

condition to be met   *key date*
(1) ....
(2) ....
(3) .... |
| 71 | **If Option C, D, E or F is used**
This is an optional statement. See question 39 above. For all main Options except Options A and B, the *Contractor* is required to provide regular forecasts of the total Defined Cost so that the *Project Manager* is kept up to date about the cost of the project as it progresses, as it cannot be easily measured against an *activity schedule* or *bill of quantities* as it can be in Options A and B, respectively. | ■ The *Contractor* prepares forecasts of the total Defined Cost for the whole of the *works* at intervals no longer than . . .
.... |

3. Time

72	The *starting date* is one of a series of dates specified by the *Client* in Contract Data part one and around which the *Contractor* plans the *works*. This date is not necessarily the start date on Site, but the date when work for the contract starts, e.g. design or fabrication.	■ The *starting date* is ....
73	Access is when the *Contractor* is given permission to occupy the Site. This might be after the *starting date*, if there is design or manufacture to take place first. If there is only one part of the Site, then this would be described as the 'whole of the Site'.	■ The *access dates* are part of the Site date (1) .... (2) ....
74	The *Contractor* is required to revise their programme every so often (see clause 32.2), and this statement dictates the period of time between revisions. The period stated is typically 1 month; however, each *Client* should review the frequency required against the complexity and nature of the *works*. The submission of revised programmes is a demanding activity that the *Contractor* and the *Project Manager* should work on together to achieve. For longer contracts, the interval could be a longer period of time, such as 8 weeks. The *Project Manager* always has the option to request a revision outwith the stated period of time.	■ The *Contractor* submits revised programmes at intervals no longer than . . . .
75	**If the *Client* has decided the *completion* date for the whole of the *works*** This is an optional statement. See your answer to question 40 above as to whether it should be included.	■ The *completion date* for the whole of the *works* is . . . .
76	**If the *Client* is not willing to take over the *works* before the Completion Date** This is an optional statement. See your answer to question 42 above as to whether it should be included.	■ The *Client* **is/is not** willing to take over the *works* before the Completion Date
77	**If no programme is identified in part two of the Contract Data** This is an optional statement. See your answer to question 41 above as to whether it should be included.	■ The period after the Contract Data within which the *Contractor* is to submit a first programme for acceptance is . . . .

	Statement required	Contract Data entry
4. Quality management		
78	Clause 40.2 requires the *Contractor* to provide to the *Project Manager* a quality policy statement and a quality plan for acceptance within a certain period of time after the Contract Date. Note that the *Client* does not have the choice to request these documents with the tender rather than after the Contract Date, although they have this choice with the programme and also with the Option X10 Information Execution Plan. This requirement highlights the importance of quality management and having those policy statements and quality plan in place.	■ The period after the Contract Date within which the *Contractor* is to submit a quality policy statement and quality plan is ....
79	The *Contractor* is required to correct Defects free of charge up until the *defects date*, a period of time that might traditionally have been known as the defects liability period or the maintenance period. It would usually be 52 weeks but could be 26 weeks and on process-plant-type products it could be 104 weeks. Because the *defects date* is after Completion of the whole of the *works*, *sections* of the *works* completed earlier are subject to a longer period of time for the correction of Defects. Note also that the date affects numerous provisions in the conditions as follows: ■ a payment that is conditional on a *Supervisor's* test or inspection being successful becomes due at the *defects date* (or end of the last *defect correction period* if later) under certain conditions (clause 41.5) ■ until the *defects date,* the *Supervisor* may instruct the *Contractor* to search for a Defect (clause 43.1) ■ assessing the cost of correcting Defects if the *Contractor* is not given access in order to correct a notified Defect before the *defects date* (clause 46.2) ■ submitting insurance certificates (clause 84.1).	■ The period between Completion of the whole of the *works* and the *defects date* is ....

80	The *Contractor* is required to correct notified Defects within a certain period of time after a Defect has been notified to them by the *Supervisor*, or after they have noticed the Defect themselves. Although this may be a standard period of time for all Defects, there may be projects where the periods of time would be different for different types of Defects. In this case, an example of the Contract Data statement follows.
	
	The *defect correction period* is
	
	■ 30 minutes for category A Defects
	■ 48 hours for category B Defects
	■ 1 week for category C Defects and
	■ 4 weeks for category D Defects
	
	where Defect categories are described in the Scope.
		■ The *defect correction period* is .... except that
		  – The *defect correction period* for .... is ....
		  – The *defect correction period* for .... is ....
		(Other bullet points may be added as required.)

5. Payment		
81	The *currency of the contract* is the currency in which the *Contractor* is paid, and would generally be the pound sterling for contracts written in the UK.	■ The *currency of this contract* is the ....
82	The *Project Manager* assesses the amount due at every assessment date. Although the first assessment date takes place to suit the procedures of the Parties, other assessment dates through the contract up to Completion tend to take place every period of time. This period of time could be ■ 'one calendar month', or ■ 'in accordance with the matrix of project dates included in Appendix B to this contract' (where such a schedule includes, for example, assessment dates, certificate dates, invoice dates and payments dates), or ■ '4 weeks', in which case the assessment would be slightly earlier every month since some months contain more than 4 weeks.	■ The *assessment interval* is ....

	Statement required	Contract Data entry
83	The *Client* pays interest if they pay the *Contractor* later than they should. Interest is calculated from the date by which payment should have been made until the date when payment is made, and is compounded annually. The fact that the rate is stated as a percentage above the rate of the specified bank allows for the fluctuation of interest rates during the performance of the contract. The interest rate is likely to be '2% above the standard base rate of a bank, e.g. The Royal Bank of Scotland', or something similar. Try to avoid using averages of many banks if possible, since it increases the workload unnecessarily, and introduces conflict, since there are at least three different ways of calculating an average. It should be noted that the commercial rate of interest may be deemed to be nearer 8%.	■ The *interest rate* is .... % per annum (not less than 2) above the .... rate of the .... bank
84	**If the period in which payments are made is not 3 weeks and Y(UK)2 is not used** This is an optional statement. See your answer to question 43a or 43b above as to whether it should be included.	■ The period within which payments are made is ....
85	**If Option C or D is used** This is an optional statement. See your answer to question 44b above as to whether it should be included. See Chapter 2 in this book for an example.	■ The *Contractor's share percentages* and the *share ranges* are share range *Contractor's share percentage* less than ...... % ....% less than ...... % ....% less than ...... % ....% less than ...... % ....%
86	**If Option C, D, E or F is used** This is an optional statement. See your answer to question 44a above as to whether it should be included. Since the *Client* will pay the *Contractor* in other currencies if they have paid a supplier in other currencies, the base exchange rate to be used for conversion into the *currency of the contract* for the purposes of the Fee and the share must be stated.	■ The *exchange rates* are those published in .... on .... [date]

6. Compensation events

	Statement required	Contract Data entry
87	This statement is used for the compensation event in clause 60.1(13). The comparison that should take place is the weather at this place (on or near the Site) and the weather at the place where it was recorded. This place should therefore be on or as near to the Site as possible in order for the *Contractor* to be able to ascertain the effect of the weather on their work at the Site.	■ The place where weather is to be recorded is ....

88	These are the aspects of the weather that could affect the *Contractor* in their Providing the Works. They are to be measured at the Site in order to facilitate a comparison with the *weather data* at the place where they were recorded (as stated in item 61 above). An example of additional measurements is wind, where there is cranage; however, if there are no extra measurements, then the last bullet point should be deleted.	■ The *weather measurements* to be recorded for each calendar month are
		  – the cumulative rainfall (mm)
		  – the number of days with rainfall more than 5 mm
		  – the number of days with minimum air temperature less than 0 degrees Celsius
		  – the number of days with snow lying at .... hours GMT
		  – and these measurements: ....

89	The *Client* has an opportunity to state who will be taking the weather measurements throughout the period of the contract. This could be the *Contractor*, the *Client* or a third party. The Met Office has a dedicated section on NEC contracts.	■ The *weather measurements* are supplied by ....

	Statement required	Contract Data entry
90a	This is the place where the comparative data were recorded. It should also be as near to the Site as possible. Where you have no data, the next Contract Data statement should be used and this one deleted.	■ The *weather data* are the records of past *weather measurements* for each calendar month which were recorded at .... and which are available from ....
90b	**Where no recorded data are available** This is an optional statement. See your answer to question 45 above as to whether it should be included. Where you have no data to compare the current weather at the Site, you should assume values. In this case, delete the previous Contract Data statement and include this one.	■ Assumed values for the 10-year return *weather data* for each *weather measurement* for each calendar month are ....
91	**If Option A or B is used** This is an optional statement. See your answer to question 46 above as to whether it should be included. ECC4 provides the opportunity for the *Contractor* to be rewarded for putting forward value engineering ideas.	■ The *value engineering percentage* is 50%, unless another percentage is stated here, in which case it is .... %
92	**If Option B or D is used** This is an optional statement. See your answer to question 47 above as to whether it should be included. Decide the *method of measurement* to apply to the *bill of quantities.*	■ The *method of measurement* is ....
93	**If there are additional compensation events** This is an optional statement. See your answer to question 48 above as to whether it should be included.	■ These are additional compensation events ....

7. Title

94	There are no Contract Data entries required for this section of the core clauses, but in order to retain the chronological numbering of the Contract Data, you might want to include a statement to this effect.	There are no Contract Data entries required for this section of the core clauses.

8. Liabilities and insurance

95	**If there are additional *Client's* liabilities** This is an optional statement. See your answer to question 49 above as to whether it should be included.	■ These are additional *Client* liabilities (1) .... (2) .... (3) ....
96	This Contract Data statement correlates with the third statement in the Insurance Table included in clause 83.3, and the amount of insurance required should be stated here. The clause refers to the loss or damage specifically arising from the *Contractor* Providing the Works.	■ The minimum amount of cover for insurance against loss of or damage to property (except the *works*, Plant and Materials and Equipment) and liability for bodily injury to or death of a person (not an employee of the *Contractor*) arising from or in connection with the *Contractor* Providing the Works for any one event is ....
97	This correlates with the fourth statement in the Insurance Table, and the amount of insurance required should be stated here. The contract specifically refers to 'any one event'.	■ The minimum limit of cover for insurance against death of or bodily injury to employees of the *Contractor* arising out of and in the course of their employment in connection with the contract for any one event is ....

	Statement required	Contract Data entry
98	**If the *Client* is to provide Plant and Materials** This is an optional statement. See your answer to question 50 above as to whether it should be included.	■ The insurance against loss of or damage to the *works*, Plant and Materials is to include cover for Plant and Materials provided by the *Client* for an amount of . . . .
99	**If the *Client* is to provide any of the insurances stated in the Insurance Table** This is an optional statement. See your answer to question 51 above as to whether it should be included.	■ The *Client* provides these insurances from the Insurance Table (1) Insurance against . . . . Minimum amount of cover is . . . . . . The deductibles are . . . . (2) Insurance against . . . . Minimum amount of cover is . . . . . . The deductibles are . . . .
100	**If the *Client* intends to provide additional insurances are to be provided** This is an optional statement. See your answer to question 52 above as to whether it should be included.	■ The *Client* provides these additional insurances (1) Insurance against . . . . Minimum amount of cover is . . . . . . The deductibles are . . . . (2) Insurance against . . . . Minimum amount of cover is . . . . . . The deductibles are . . . .
101	**If the *Client* requires the *Contractor* to provide additional insurances** This is an optional statement. See your answer to question 53 above as to whether it should be included.	■ The *Contractor* provides these additional insurances (1) Insurance against . . . . Minimum amount of cover is . . . . . . The deductibles are . . . . (2) Insurance against . . . . Minimum amount of cover is . . . . . . The deductibles are . . . .

9. Resolving and avoiding disputes

102	No matter whether Option W1, W2 or W3 is chosen, the *Client* still needs to decide whether the next form of dispute resolution – called the *tribunal* – is arbitration or litigation. If the *tribunal* is arbitration, then there are other Contract Data part one entries to complete. Question 3 above pertains to this Contract Data entry.	■ The *tribunal* is . . . .
103	**If the *tribunal* is arbitration** These are optional statements. If you have chosen arbitration as your *tribunal*, then these statements should be included here in the Contract Data. If the *tribunal* is not arbitration, then none of these statements is required in Contract Data part one. Question 4 above pertains to this Contract Data entry.	■ The *arbitration procedure* is . . . . ■ The place where arbitration is to be held is . . . . ■ The person or organisation who will choose an arbitrator if the Parties cannot agree a choice or if the *arbitration procedure* does not state who selects an arbitrator is . . . .
104	These next few statements depend on whether the *Client* has chosen Option W1, W2 or W3 for the contract. Questions 5–7 above pertain to this Contract Data entry.	

	Statement required	Contract Data entry
105a	**If Option W1 or W2 is used** Questions 5 and 6 pertain to this Contract Data entry. Options W1 and W2 both use the *Senior Representatives* and the *Adjudicator* as the first and second tiers of dispute resolution. Option W2 is used with contracts in the UK to which the HGCR Act is applied, and although the *Senior Representatives* are the first tier of dispute resolution, the referral of a dispute to the *Senior Representatives* prior to a referral to the *Adjudicator* cannot be mandated as the HCGR Act allows the Parties to refer a dispute to adjudication at any time. Both Options W1 and W2 allow the facility for someone else to choose an adjudicator, if ■ the *Adjudicator* is not identified in the Contract Data or ■ the *Adjudicator* resigns or becomes unable to act.	■ The *Senior Representatives* of the *Client* are Name (1) .... Address for communications .... Address for electronic communications .... Name (2) .... Address for communications .... Address for electronic communications .... ■ The *Adjudicator* is Name .... Address for communications .... Address for electronic communications .... ■ The *Adjudicator nominating body* is ... .
105b	**If Option W3 is used Question 7 pertains to this Contract Data entry**	■ The *Client's* nomination for the Dispute Avoidance Board is Name .... Address for electronic communications .... ■ The Dispute Avoidance Board visit the Site at intervals no longer than ......months ■ The *Dispute Avoidance Board nominating body* is ....
	Statements for secondary Option clauses	
106	**Option X1, 'Price adjustment for inflation (used only with Options A, B, C and D)'** **If Option X1 is used** This is an optional statement. See your answer to question 10 above as to whether it should be included. Statement for Option X1 only with Options A, B, C and D.	■ The proportions used to calculate the Price Adjustment Factor are 0 ..... linked to the index for .... 0 ..... non-adjustable .... 1.00 ■ The *base date* for indices is .... ■ The indices are ....
107	**Option X2, 'Changes in the law'** See your answer to question 11 as to whether you have chosen this option.	There are no Contract Data entries for Option X2.
108	**Option X3, 'Multiple currency used only with Options A and B'** **If Option X3 is used** This is an optional statement. See your answer to question 12 above as to whether it should be included. Statement for Option X3 only.	■ The *Client* will pay for the items or activities listed below in the currencies stated. | items and activities	other currency	total maximum payment in the currency
....	....	....
....	....	.... | ■ The *exchange rates* are those published in .... on .... [date]

	Statement required	Contract Data entry
109	**Option X4, 'Ultimate holding company guarantee'** See your answer to question 13 as to whether you have chosen this option.	There are no Contract Data entries for Option X4.
110	**Option X5, 'Sectional Completion'** **If Option X5 is used** This is an optional statement. See your answer to question 14 above as to whether it should be included. Statement for Option X5 only. What *sections* of the work are there and when do you want them to be completed? Generally, the last section should not be the end of the project but one stage before, since Completion is defined elsewhere.	■ The *completion date* for each section of the works is *section* description *completion date* (1) .... (2) .... (3) .... (4) ....
111a	**Option X6, 'Bonus for early Completion'** **If Option X6 is used without Option X5** This is an optional statement. See your answer to question 15 above as to whether it should be included. This Contract Data statement should only be included where Option X6 is chosen and Option X5 is **not** chosen.	■ The bonus for the whole of the *works* is ....
111b	**If Option X6 is used with Option X5** This is an optional statement. This Contract Data statement should only be included where Options X5 and X6 are both chosen. If only Option X5 **or** X6 (or neither) is chosen, then this statement should be deleted. The same sections as described in item 110 above should be stated.	■ The bonus for each *section* of the *works* is *section* description amount per day (1) .... (2) .... (3) .... (4) .... ■ The bonus for the remainder of the *works* is ....
112a	**Option 7, 'Delay Damages'** **If Option X7 is used without Option X5** This is an optional statement. See your answer to question 16 above as to whether it should be included. This Contract Data statement should only be included where Option X7 is chosen and Option X5 is **not** chosen.	■ Delay damages for Completion of the whole of the *works* are .... per day
112b	**If Option X7 is used with Option X5** This is an optional statement. This Contract Data statement should only be included where Options X5 and X7 are both chosen. If only X5 **or** X7 is chosen, then this statement should be deleted. The same sections as in item 110 above should be stated.	■ Delay damages for each *section* of the *works* are *section* description amount per day (1) .... (2) .... (3) .... (4) .... ■ The delay damages for the remainder of the *works* are ....
113	**Option X8, 'Undertakings to the *Client* or Others'** **If Option X8 is used** This is an optional statement. See your answer to question 17 as to whether you have chosen this Option.	■ The *undertakings* to *Others* are provided to .... ■ The *Subcontractor undertaking to Others* are works provided to .... ■ The *Subcontractor undertaking to the Client* are works ....

	Statement required	Contract Data entry
114	**Option X9, 'Transfer of rights'** See your answer to question 18 as to whether you have chosen this option.	There are no Contract Data entries for Option X9.
115	**Option X10, 'Information modelling'** **If Option X10 is used** This is an optional statement. See your answer to question 19 as to whether you have chosen this option. Question 35 also provides guidance. This statement is used if no Information Execution Plan is identified in Contract Data part two.	**If no BIM execution plan is identified in part two of the Contract Data** ■ The period after the Contract Date within which the *Contractor* is to submit a first Information Execution Plan for acceptance is .... ■ The minimum amount of insurance cover for claims made against the *Contractor* arising out of its failure to use the skill and care normally used by professionals providing information similar to the Project Information is, in respect of each claim .... ■ The period following Completion of the whole of the *works* or earlier termination for which the *Contractor* maintains insurance for claims made against it arising out its failure to use the skill and are is ....
116	**Option X11, 'Termination by the *Client*'** See your answer to question 20 as to whether you have chosen this option.	There are no Contract Data entries for Option X11.
117	**Option X12, 'Multiparty collaboration (not used with Option X20)'** **If Option X12 is used** This is an optional statement. See your answer to question 21 above as to whether it should be included.	■ The Schedule of Partners is in .... ■ The *Client's* objective is in .... ■ The Partnering Information is in ....
118	**Option X13, 'Performance bond'** **If Option X13 is used** This is an optional statement. See your answer to question 22 above as to whether it should be included.	■ The amount of the performance bond is ....
119	**Option X14, 'Advanced payment to the *Contractor*'** **If Option X14 is used** This is an optional statement. See your answer to question 23 above as to whether it should be included.	■ The amount of the advanced payment is .... ■ The period after the Contract Date from which the *Contractor* repays the instalments in assessments is .... ■ The instalments are .... (either an amount or a percentage of the payment otherwise due) **If the *Contractor* is to provide an advance payment bond** ■ The *Contractor* is to provide an advanced payment bond.
120	**Option X15, 'The *Contractor's* design'** **If Option X15 is used** This is an optional statement. See your answer to question 24 above as to whether it should be included.	■ The *period for retention* following Completion of the whole of the *works* or earlier termination is .... ■ The minimum amount of insurance cover for claims made against the *Contractor* arising out of its failure to

	Statement required	Contract Data entry
		use the skill and care normally used by professionals designing works similar to the *works* is, in respect of each claim ....
		■ The period following Completion of the whole of the *works* or earlier termination for which the *Contractor* maintains insurance for claims made against it arising out of its failure to use the skill and are is ....
121	**Option X16, 'Retention (not used with Option F)'** **If Option X16 is used** This is an optional statement. See your answer to question 25 above as to whether it should be included. Statements for Option X16 only.	■ The *retention free* amount is .... ■ The *retention percentage* is .... % **If the *Contractor* may give the *Client* a retention bond** ■ The *Contractor* may give the *Client* a retention bond.
122	**Option X17, 'Low performance damages'** **If Option X17 is used** This is an optional statement. See your answer to question 26 above as to whether it should be included. Statement for Option X17.	■ The amounts for low-performance damages are amount performance level .... for .... for .... for ....
123	**Option X18, 'Limitation of liability'** **If Option X18 is used** This is an optional statement. See your answer to question 27 above as to whether it should be included. Statement for Option X18.	■ The *Contractor's* liability to the *Client* for indirect or consequential loss is limited to.............................. ■ For any one event the *Contractor's* liability to the *Client* for loss of or damage to the *Client's* property is limited to.............................. ■ The *Contractor's* liability for Defects due to its design which are not listed on the Defects Certificate is limited to .... ■ The *Contractor's* total liability to the *Client* for all matters arising under or in connection with the contract, other than excluded matters, is limited to .... ■ The *end of liability date* is .... years after the Completion of the whole of the *works*.
124	Option X19 is not used in the ECC.	
125	**Option X20, 'Key Performance Indicators (not used with Option X12)'** **If Option X20 is used** This is an optional statement. See your answer to question 28 above as to whether it should be included. This Option may not be used if Option X12 is used.	■ The *incentive schedule* for Key Performance Indicators is in .... ■ A report of performance against each Key Performance Indicator is provided at intervals of .... months
126	**Option X21, 'Whole life cost'** See your answer to question 29 as to whether you have chosen this option.	There are no Contract Data entries for Option X21.

	Statement required	Contract Data entry
127	**Option X22, 'Early *Contractor* involvement'** **If Option X22 is used** See your answer to question 30 above as to whether you have chosen this Option.	■ The Budget is item description amount (1) .... (2) .... (3) .... (4) .... Total .... ■ The *Contractor* prepares forecasts of the total Defined Cost of the work to be done in Stage One at intervals no longer than .... ■ The *Contractor* prepares forecasts of the total Project Cost at intervals no longer than .... **If there are additional events which could change the Budget** ■ These are additional events which could change the Budget (1) .... (2) .... (3) .... ■ The *budget incentive* is ......% of the saving
128	**Option Y(UK)1, 'Project Bank Account'** **If Option Y(UK)1 is used and the *Client* is to pay any charges made and is paid any interest paid by the *project bank*** This is an optional statement. See your answer to question 31 above as to whether it should be included.	■ The *Client* is to pay any charges made and is paid any interest paid by the *project bank*
129	**Option Y(UK)2, 'The Housing Grants, Construction and Regeneration Act 1996'** **If Y(UK)2 is used and the final date for payment is not 14 days after the date which payment becomes due** This is an optional statement. See your answer to questions 32 and 43b above as to whether it should be included.	■ The period for payment is .... days after the date on which payment becomes due
130	**Option Y(UK)3, 'The Contracts (Rights of Third Parties) Act 1999'** **If Option Y(UK)3 is used** This is an optional statement. See your answer to question 33 as to whether you have chosen this Option.	
131	**If Option Y(UK)3 is used with Y(UK)1** This entry is added to the table for Option Y(UK)3. See your answer to questions 128 and 130 above.	■ term .... beneficiary .... The provisions of Named Suppliers Option Y(UK)1
132	**Option Z, '*Additional conditions of contract*'** **If Option Z is used** This is an optional statement. See your answer to question 34 above as to whether it should be included.	■ The *additional conditions of contract* are ....

3.7.2 Contract Data part two by the *Contractor*

The *Client* should remember to choose the correct statements for Contract Data part two, depending on what Options apply to the contract and whether the following apply:

- the *Contractor's* design proposals are submitted with the tender
- the programme is with the tender
- the *Contractor* is to dictate the *completion date*
- the data for the Schedule of Cost Components might change if you have used Option Z to amend the Schedule of Cost Components in the contract.

The following items relate to each Contract Data part two entry as it appears in the ECC. Some of the entries are decided by the *Client*, and all Contract Data entries are completed by the *Contractor* at the tender stage.

	Statement required	Contract Data entry
1. General		
133	The *Contractor* completes this entry at the tender stage. It completes the name of its company and the required addresses.	■ The *Contractor* is Name . . . . Address for communications . . . . Address for electronic communications . . . .
134	The *Contractor* completes this entry at tender stage. The *fee percentage* represents the *Contractor's* profits and overheads that do not already appear in the Schedule of Cost Components for work that is not subcontracted. This entry should be completed no matter what main Option is chosen by the *Client*.	■ The *fee percentage* is . . . . %
135	The *Contractor* completes this entry at the tender stage. The *working areas* are very important in defining the *Contractor's* costs, and thought should be given as to what should be included in the *working areas*, along with the Site. The *working areas* are those areas within which the *Contractor* can apply for Defined Cost, whether for a compensation event or during the period of the contract. They should therefore not include the *Contractor's* head office, but should include any prefabrication workshops next to the Site. See Chapter 2 of Book Four on the Schedule of Cost Components for further discussion.	■ The *working areas* are . . . .
136	The *Contractor* completes this entry at the tender stage. The people who work on the project can make or break the contract, and it is important for the *Client* to see who they will be working with and their qualifications and experience. If the *Contractor* wishes to replace these people, the substitutes should be as, if not more, qualified and experienced than the *key persons*. The *Contractor* should therefore ensure that the people named at the tender stage will be available for the contract.	■ The *key persons* are Name (1) . . . . Job . . . . Responsibilities . . . . Qualifications . . . . Experience . . . . Name (2) . . . . term beneficiary . . . .
137	The *Contractor* completes this entry at the tender stage. The Early Warning Register includes risks that are listed in the Contract Data. The *Client* has an opportunity to list risks to be included in the Early Warning Register in their Contract Data part one. The *Contractor* has the same opportunity to list in Contract Data part two what they consider to be risks.	■ The following matters will be included in the Early Warning Register . . . .

	Statement required	Contract Data entry
2. The *Contractor's* main responsibilities		
138	The *Client* chooses whether to include this entry. See your answer to question 54 above. This is an **optional statement** that should be used where the *Contractor* is providing information for their design, where design is part of their scope of work. The *Client* should delete the entire entry if there is no design involved or if the *Contractor* does not provide information for their design with their tender. The *Contractor* completes this Contract Data entry by stating where their design proposal can be located within their tender document, e.g. 'The Scope provided by the *Contractor* for its design is in the document entitled "*Contractor's* proposal".' This Scope will then be included in the contract as the Scope by the *Contractor*, and any change to this Scope made at the *Contractor's* request, to comply with the law or the *Client's* Scope, is not a compensation event.	**If the *Contractor* is to provide Scope for its design** ■ The Scope provided by the *Contractor* for its design is in . . . .
3. Time		
139	The *Client* chooses whether to include this entry. See your answer to question 55 and refer to 77 and 41 above. This is an **optional statement** that is included only when the optional statement for the programme is not included in Contract Data part one. The statements are in the alternative, thus: ■ If the *Client* wants to see a programme with the tender, it will choose this optional statement in Contract Data part two and will not include the equivalent statement in Contract Data part one. ■ If the *Client* does not want to see a programme with the tender, but would rather see the first programme a period of time after the Contract Date, it will choose the statement in Contract Data part one and it will delete this statement about the programme in Contract Data part two. The *Contractor* should complete this entry by stating where their tender programme can be located in their tender package, e.g. 'The programme identified in the Contract Data is in the document entitled "Programme for the *works*".'	**If a programme is to be identified in the Contract Data** ■ The programme identified in the Contract Data is . . . .
140	The *Client* chooses whether to include this entry. See your answer to question 56 above. This is an **optional statement** that is chosen only if the *Client* has not chosen a *completion date* in Contract Data part one. The statements are in the alternative, thus: ■ If the *Client* wants to dictate the *completion date* for the whole of the *works*, it will choose the statement in Contract Data part one and it will delete this statement about the *completion date* in Contract Data part two (see question 75 and 40 above). ■ If the *Client* is content for the tenderer to dictate the *completion date* based on the tenderer's interpretation of the Scope and the tenderer's programme, it will choose this optional statement in Contract Data part two and will delete the equivalent statement in Contract Data part one. The *Contractor* should complete this Contract Data entry by stating the date by which it thinks it can achieve Completion. This date should also be included in its programme and should allow for any terminal float, i.e. the *Contractor* should include planned Completion as well as Completion in their programme.	**If the *Contractor* is to decide the *completion date* for the whole of the *works*** ■ The *completion date* for the whole of the *works* is . . . .

	Statement required	Contract Data entry
4. Quality management		
141		No Contract Data part two exists for this section
5. Payment		
142	**If Option A or C is used** The *Client* chooses to include this entry when Option A or C is the chosen main Option. The *Contractor* completes this entry by stating where the *activity schedule* can be found in their tender package, e.g. 'The *activity schedule* is in the document entitled "Activity Schedule".'	■ The *activity schedule* is ....
143	**If Option B or D is used** The *Client* chooses to include this entry when Option B or D is the chosen main Option. The *Contractor* completes this entry by stating where the *bill of quantities* can be found in their tender package, e.g. 'The *bill of quantities* is in the document entitled "Bill of Quantities".'	■ The *bill of quantities* is ....
	If Option A, B, C or D is used The *Client* chooses to include this entry when Option A, B, C or D is the chosen main Option. The *Contractor* should also include the tendered total of the Prices, i.e. ■ for Options A and C: the sum of all the lumps sum prices in the *activity schedule* ■ for Options B or D: the sum of all the rates-item product in the *bill of quantities*.	■ The tendered total of the Prices is ....
144	**If Option F is used** The *Client* chooses whether to include this entry when Option F is the chosen main Option. Clause 20.2 states that the *Contractor* will subcontract the *Contractor's* design, the provision of the Site services and the construction and installation of the *works*, except work that the Contract Data states that it will do. The *Contractor* should therefore include in their tender the aspects of the *works* which it intends to carry out itself.	■ Work which the *Contractor* will do is .... activity *price* ....
Resolving and avoiding disputes		
145	**If Option W1 or W2 is used** The *Client* chooses whether to include this entry. See your answer to questions 3–7 above. The *Client* includes this entry in the Contract Data if they have chosen Option W1 or W2 as the resolving and avoiding disputes option. The *Client* lists their nominations for the *Senior Representatives* in Contract Data part one and includes this entry in Contract Data part two to be completed by the *Contractor* at tender stage. The *Contractor* inserts their nominations for the *Senior Representatives* to represent the *Contractor* for the first tier of dispute resolution.	■ The *Senior Representatives* of the *Contractor* are Name (1) .... Address for communications .... Address for electronic communications .... Name (2) .... Address for communications .... Address for electronic communications ....

	Statement required	Contract Data entry
146	**If Option W3 is used** The *Client* chooses whether to include this entry. See your answer to questions 3–7 above. The *Client* includes this entry in the Contract Data if they have chosen Option W3 as the resolving and avoiding disputes option. The *Client* lists their nomination for the Dispute Avoidance Board in Contract Data part one and includes this entry in Contract Data part two to be completed by the *Contractor* at tender stage. The *Contractor* inserts their nominations for the Dispute Avoidance Board to represent the *Contractor* for the first tier of dispute resolution.	■ The *Contractor's* nomination for the Dispute Avoidance Board is Name .... Address for electronic communications ....

Secondary Options

	Statement required	Contract Data entry
147	**Option X10, 'Information modelling'** **If Option X10 is used** The *Client* chooses whether to include this entry. See your answer to question 19 above. This is an **optional statement** that is included only when the optional statement for the Information Execution Plan is not included in Contract Data part one. The statements are in the alternative, thus: ■ If the *Client* wants to see an Information Execution Plan with the tender, it will choose this optional statement in Contract Data part two and will not include the equivalent statement in Contract Data part one. ■ If the *Client* does not want to see an Information Execution Plan with the tender, but would rather see the first programme a period of time after the Contract Date, it will choose the statement in Contract Data part one and it will delete this statement about the programme in Contract Data part two. The *Contractor* should complete this entry by stating where their Information Execution Plan can be located in their tender package, e.g. 'The Information Execution Plan identified in the Contract Data is in the document entitled "Information Execution Plan".'	■ The *information execution plan* identified in the Contract Data is ....
148	**Option X22, 'Early *Contractor* involvement'** **If Option X22 is used** The *Client* chooses whether to include this entry. See your answer to question 30 above. In their tender, the *Contractor* should ■ provide information in Contract Data part two about the names and other details of the people who will be involved in Stage One ■ provide information about where the *Client* can find the Pricing Information in the tender.	■ The Stage One *key persons* are Name (1) .... Job .... Responsibilities .... Experience .... Name (2) .... Job .... Responsibilities .... Experience .... ■ The Pricing Information is ....
149	**Option Y(UK)1, 'Project Bank Account'** **If Option Y(UK)1 is used** The *Client* chooses whether to include this entry. See your answer to question 31 above.	■ The *project bank* is .... ■ *named suppliers* are ....

3.7.3 Data for the Schedule of Cost Components and Short Schedule of Cost Components

Abbreviations used in this section:

- SCC: Schedule of Cost Components (used only with main Options C, D and E)
- Short SCC: Short Schedule of Cost Components (used only with main Options A and B).

Note that Option F does not use either the SCC or the Short SCC.

In ECC4, the data are presented and separated according to the main Option used in the contract. The *Client* should choose which set of data to include in Contract Data part two when it is issued with the invitation to tender, and the *Contractor* then completes that Contract Data as part of their tender.

The first set of data for the SCC to appear in the Contract Data is the data for the SCC for Options C, D or E.

3.7.3.1 Data for the SCC: if Options C, D and E is used

The following Contract Data entries are to be used with the SCC only for main Options C, D and E. The information for the SCC should be completed by the *Contractor*.

	Statement required	Contract Data entry
If Option C, D or E is used		
150	This entry correlates with cost component 23 of the SCC. The Equipment that is especially purchased for work included in the contract should be listed here. The time-related charge for the Equipment as well as the time period to which the charge relates should also be included.	■ The listed items of Equipment purchased for work on this contract, with an on cost charge, are Equipment time-related per time on cost charge period ....
151	This correlates with cost component 24 of the SCC. The *Contractor* lists here special Equipment that they intend to use, together with the rates.	■ The rates for special Equipment are Equipment rate ....
152	These entries correlate with cost component 61 of the SCC. Note that this data entry refers to the manufacture and fabrication of Plant and Materials **outside** the Working Areas (as identified by the *Contractor*). This therefore refers to manufacture and fabrication in the *Contractor's* primary place of manufacture and not any temporary fabrication shop set up near the Site (which should be identified as a Working Area). Hourly rates could be broken into normal hours (which should be identified) and overtime. Categories of employees could include welder, labourer, etc. If a supervisor is dedicated to that fabrication shop, then they could be included as a category of employee; otherwise, any supervisors that supervise all jobs and are not dedicated to the particular project should be included as an overhead.	■ The hourly rates for Defined Cost of manufacture and fabrication outside the Workings Areas are category of employee hourly rate ....
153	These entries correlate with cost components 71 and 72 of the SCC. Note that this data entry refers to costs **outside** the Working Areas (as identified by the *Contractor*). This therefore refers to design carried out in the *Contractor's* primary place of design, possibly the head office, and not any design that takes place on the Site by employees that have been relocated there. Hourly rates could be broken into normal hours (which should be identified) and overtime. Categories of employees could include technician, CAD operator, etc. The categories of employees who are required to travel to and from the Working Areas in the course of their design duties should be stated, so that the *Client* knows in advance what charges for travel will be made.	■ The rates for Defined Cost of design outside the Working Areas are category of employee hourly rate .... ■ The categories of design people whose travelling expenses to and from the Working Areas are included as a cost of design of the *works* and Equipment done outside the Working Areas are ....

3.7.3.2 Data for the Short SCC: if Options A or B are used

The following Contract Data entries are to be used with the Short SCC only for main Options A and B. The information for the Short SCC should be completed by the *Contractor*.

	Statement required	Contract Data entry
If Option A or B is used		
154	This correlates with cost component 11 – people who work within the Working Areas.	■ The *people rates* are category of person unit rate ....
155	This correlates with cost component 21 of the Short SCC. The published list should be a list in the public domain rather than an in-house published list. An example is the Civil Engineering Contractors Association (CECA) Dayworks Schedule.	■ The published list of Equipment is the edition current at the Contract Date of the list published by ....
156	This correlates with cost component 21 of the Short SCC. This percentage recognises that the rates in a published list tend to be an all-inclusive rate, thereby including profits and overheads. Because the *Contractor* is able to retrieve their profits and overheads through the *fee percentage* and the other overheads stated in the Short SCC, the rates in the published list should be reduced. If some rates are reduced by a different percentage to other rates, more than one percentage can be stated, as long as the boundaries of applicability are defined.	■ The percentage for adjustment for Equipment in the published list is ...... % (state plus or minus)
157	This correlates with cost component 22 of the Short SCC. The *Contractor* lists here other Equipment that it intends to use and that is not included in the published list.	■ The rates for other Equipment are Equipment rate ....
158	These entries correlate with cost components 71 and 72 respectively of the Short SCC. Note that this data entry refers to costs **outside** the Working Areas (as identified by the *Contractor*). This therefore refers to design in the *Contractor's* primary place of design, possibly the head office, and not any design that takes place on the Site by employees that have been relocated there. Hourly rates could be broken into normal hours (which should be identified) and overtime. Categories of employees could include technician, CAD operator, etc. The categories of employees who are required to travel to and from the Working Areas in the course of their design duties should be stated so that the *Client* knows in advance what charges for travel will be made.	■ The hourly rates for Defined Cost of design outside the Working Areas are category of employee hourly rate .... ■ The categories of design employees whose traveling expenses to and from the Working Areas are included in Defined Cost are ....

Procuring an Engineering and Construction Contract
ISBN 978-0-7277-6184-2

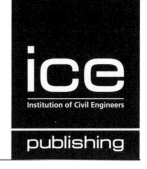

Chapter 4
Scope guidelines

Synopsis

This chapter looks at the Scope and Site Information, including

- Providing the Works
- what should be included in the Scope
- separation of the Scope and the Site Information
- structuring for the Scope
- interface management
- general rules in drafting the Scope
- Site Information.

4.1. Introduction

The documents within an NEC contract all interact with each other, and are therefore required to be drafted in such a manner that they complement each other and are related where indicated. It should also be borne in mind that there is no hierarchy of documents in the ECC. The *conditions of contract* frequently refer to information that is required to be specified within the Scope and identified in the Contract Data. It is essential that this information appears within these sections of the contract in order to create the links between the documents that make the contract work. If the information does not appear as indicated, ambiguities may arise and the *Client* or the *Contractor* may be unfairly disadvantaged.

The purpose of this chapter is to identify those clauses within the *conditions of contract* that refer to information that is required to appear in the Scope. This chapter also discusses the requirements of these clauses and how they could be incorporated into the Scope.

The vast majority of disputes arise as a result of the Scope and the management of it. As the single greatest cause of disputes, it is vital to ensure that the Scope includes everything the *Client* requires, and that sufficient time and effort are spent in getting the Scope as accurate and complete as possible.

This chapter also discusses the Site Information and what is to be included in it. The way in which the Site Information relates to compensation events is also discussed.

4.2. Providing the Works

The *Contractor's* overriding obligation is in clause 20.1, which states that the *Contractor* is required to Provide the Works in accordance with the Scope. This emphasises the importance of the Scope: the *Contractor* is only obliged to do those things that the Scope states they are to do. If it is not in the Scope, they do not have an obligation to do it.

> The *Contractor's* overriding obligation is to Provide the Works in accordance with the Scope.

4.3. What should be included in the Scope

Clauses 11.2(6), 11.2(15) and 11.2(16) all describe what should be included in the Scope.

■ The *Contractor* is required to complete the *works* in accordance with the contract and all incidental work, services and actions required by the contract.
■ The Scope specifies and describes the *works* or states any constraints on how the *Contractor* Provides the Works. Further notes on the practicalities of drafting the Scope to achieve these objectives are given in this chapter.
■ A Defect has a very specific meaning under the ECC. A Defect is a part of the *works* that is not in accordance with the Scope, or a part of the *works* designed by the *Contractor* that is not in accordance with the applicable law or with the *Contractor's* design that has been accepted by the *Project Manager*. In other words, if the *Client* requires something to be done, it should be included in the Scope. If it has not been included, then its absence cannot be a Defect under the contract, and the correction of a 'defect' for its absence would be reimbursable as a compensation event.
■ The description of the *works* is to be found in the Contract Data part one. This description should be as comprehensive as possible, including all aspects of the design, supply, installation, testing and commissioning of the item, particularly bearing in mind the insurance clauses.

> Imagine a situation in which the *Supervisor* notifies the *Contractor* that the reinstatement of carriageways on a utility diversion project is not to the highway authority's usual standards. However, the Scope is silent about the quality of the reinstatement.
>
> The test of a Defect is also whether the work is in accordance with the applicable law. In this instance, the reinstatement is not in accordance with the Road and Street Works Act 1991.

> A Defect is a part of the *works* that is not in accordance with the Scope.

> A Defect can be a part of the *works* designed by the *Contractor* that is not in accordance with the applicable law or with the *Contractor's* design that has been accepted by the *Project Manager*.

4.4. Separation of the Scope and Site Information

To maintain the clarity and simplicity required under the contract, it is best to ensure that the Scope and Site Information are kept separately from each other. Traditionally, work specifications and the like have tended to be jumbled together such that the information pertaining to a part of the *works* might be scattered in several locations in the contract documents and could be a mix of both Scope and Site Information. This could create confusion since the *Contractor's* obligations regarding the Scope and the Site Information are different.

Ideally, the Scope and Site Information would be in clearly defined, separate documents. However, we rarely live in an ideal world, and in some instances drawings will contain both Scope and Site Information. In such circumstances this needs to be clearly identified and some distinction shown for these drawings, perhaps by means of an asterisk or other label to show that these drawings contain a mix of both the Scope and Site Information.

The drawings will then need to be listed in both the Scope and Site Information drawing list, marked with the special reference chosen, for example

Scope – Example Drawing List

Drawing No.	Description	Rev
0100	New Work	0
0200*	Work to Existing Factory	0

Note: *Denotes a drawing containing both the Scope and Site Information

Site Information – Example Drawing List

Drawing No.	Description	Rev
500	Plan of Existing Factory	A
0200*	Work to Existing Factory	0

Note: *Denotes a drawing containing both the Scope and Site Information

> The Scope and Site Information should be kept in separate documents.

4.5. Where the Scope fits into the contract documents

The typical NEC ECC contract documents are

- the form of contract/articles of agreement
- Contract Data parts one and two
- the pricing document (e.g. the *activity schedule* or *bill of quantities*)
- the Scope
- Site Information.

Note that the Scope is separate from both the information about the Site and the contract particulars as stated in the Contract Data.

The *Client's* Scope and Site Information could comprise the following:

Volume 1A	Scope Section A General (May include typical traditional preliminary items)
Volume 1B	Scope Specification Sections B to Y (Traditional materials and workmanship specifications)
Volume 1C	Scope Specification Sections Z *Client's* requirements for the *Contractor's* designed work (The ECC relies on the Scope to clearly demarcate *Client-* and *Contractor-*designed *works*)
Volume 1D	Scope Safety, health and welfare requirements
Volume 1E	Scope Reinforcement bending schedules
Volume 2	Site Information
Drawings	Refer Appendix A of specification Section A and Appendix A of Site Information

---

If the *Contractor* is to provide the Scope for their design, then there will be an optional statement in Contract Data part two, which requires them to identify where the Scope for their design can be found, for example

The Scope provided by the *Contractor* for their design is in document **Reference Contract 123/20XX**

This information will be sent with their tender and will form part of the Scope for the contract once negotiations have been concluded.

4.6 Structuring the Scope

The Scope specifies and describes the *works*. Therefore, it will cover items such as

- the general scope (preliminaries)
- work specifications
- the *Client's* requirements for *Contractor*-designed work
- safety, health and welfare requirements
- reinforcement schedules
- drawings.

It will state the restraints, restrictions and obligations of the Parties. The Scope may also include the Scope by the *Contractor*, where the contract is a design-and-build contract and the *Contractor* has tendered a *Contractor's* proposal that meets the *Client's* requirements stated elsewhere in the Scope. The *Contractor's* proposal forms part of the Scope because it details how the *Contractor* intends to Provide the Works, but changes to it are not compensation events (clause 60.1(1)). The Scope by the *Contractor* should be kept separate from the Scope by the *Client*.

Further details of some of the items that could be included in the Scope follow.

4.6.1 Scope – general

A typical layout and type of items for this section is as follows:

- brief description of the *works*
- provision, content and use of documents

- management of the *works*
- management and staff
- quality management
- security and protection
- facilities and services to be provided by the *Contractor* for use by the *Client* and Others
- facilities and services to be provided by the *Contractor* for their own use
- facilities and services to be provided by the *Client* for use by the *Contractor*
- work by Others with whom the *Contractor* shares the Working Areas
- property in excavated materials or demolished buildings
- marking Equipment, Plant and Materials.

Note that this section does not include contract particulars, as it would do with a traditional contract, since the contract information is included in the Contract Data. The contract information given in the Contract Data is not the Scope or Site Information, and there should be no contractual information or commercial terms in the Scope.

On repetitive-type work or on framework-type arrangements where a number of similar-type contracts are to be let, it may be more appropriate to separate the Scope into

- a generic Scope (common to all contracts)
- a contract-specific Scope.

This type of approach can save much time and effort and duplication of information.

4.6.1.1 Description of the *works*

A general description for the whole of the *works* should be given, including the *Client's* objectives, followed by a detailed description of the scope of the *works*. The failure to detail here a part of the *works*, even if it is given in great detail elsewhere in the document, could be construed as being an ambiguity or inconsistency, which could give rise to a compensation event.

The *works* could include *Contractor*-designed elements of the *works*, which should also be referred to, although they are detailed later in the Scope.

The general description of the *works* should state the outline particulars of the design for those parts of the *works* not fully designed prior to award of the contract and prior to any assumptions that the *Contractor* should have allowed for in their tendered price.

This section should also include

- general arrangement and location drawings
- references to working/production and other detailed drawings, specification, models and other means to describe the parts of the *works* designed by the *Client*
- a statement of any constraints on how the *Contractor* Provides the Works, such as sequences of construction or restrictions on access.

4.6.1.2 Management of the *works*

This will cover aspects such as site progress meetings where the following issues may be discussed:

- administration of insurances
- industrial relations
- risk management
- accounts and records to be kept (depending on the main Option chosen)
- procurement procedures (depending on the main Option chosen).

It should state all the specific requirements of the *Client's* team, including IT compatibility and the like.

4.6.1.3 Programme

Clause 31.2 of the *conditions of contract* includes for any other information stated in the Scope that the *Contractor* is required to show in their programme. On multi-contract projects, this could include boundary data, foundation design data and similar information relating to their design for the use of the *Client* and other contractors. The Scope should clearly state that these dates be shown in the programme. Information about the management of the programme could also be included here.

4.6.1.4 Completion

Clause 11.2(2) requires the level of completion to be specified by the *Client*. There is no 'substantial completion', 'practical completion' or 'mechanical completion' as in traditional forms of contract. This means that Completion must be clearly defined in the Scope so that the *Contractor* knows when Completion is reached and so that the *Project Manager* knows when to certify Completion.

Clause 11.2(2) includes a default position whereby if the work that the *Contractor* is to do by the Completion Date is not stated in the Scope, Completion is when the *Contractor* has done all the work necessary for the *Client* to use the *works* and for Others to do their work. This lessens the onus on the *Client* to ensure that a description of Completion is included in the Scope.

Completion is a status that occurs when the *Project Manager* decides it has occurred (clause 30.2). In order to decide that Completion has occurred, the *Project Manager* would need a definitive statement indicating what has to be achieved before Completion has occurred. It is worth noting that there is no obligation for the *Contractor* to notify Completion.

Completion is when the following has been done by the Completion Date:

(*a*) list of the work required to be done by the Completion Date for the whole of the works and for each of the sections

or

Completion is when the *Contractor* has done everything required to Provide the Works except:

(*a*) list of work, which can remain undone at the Completion Date.

Completion cannot occur if Defects exist that would prevent the *Client* from using the *works* (clause 11.2(2)) or Others from doing their work (clause 11.2(2)). In addition, it is likely that there will be Defects that have not yet been corrected by Completion because the *Contractor* may use discretion as to which notified Defects to correct before Completion (clause 44.2). This part of the definition becomes superfluous if clause 44.2 is amended as recommended (see Chapter 3 of Book Three).

4.6.1.5 Take over

Before the Completion Date

The *Client* can choose not to take over the *works* if Completion occurs before the Completion Date. If this is the case, the *Client* states this in Contract Data part one.

Use of part of the *works*

According to clause 35.2, the *Client* is deemed to have taken over any part of the *works* where it uses that part before Completion unless the reason for the use is stated in the Scope. If it is envisaged that the *Client* might use a part of the *works* without wishing to have taken it over, then the reason for the use should be stated in the Scope. When the *Client* takes over the *works* early, delay damages should be reduced.

The *Client* will require the use of the following part of the *works* prior to Completion:

(*a*) the new car park areas as shown on drawing ABC/20XX/125A
(*b*) the new entrance to the Site as shown on drawing ABC/20XX/135B

for the following reason ....

4.6.1.6 Accounts and records

The *Contractor* is required to keep other records as stated in the Scope (clause 52.2 for Options C, D and E; clause 52.3 for Option F). The Scope should therefore state what records are to be kept, other than those in clause 52.2.

> The following is a list of accounts and records to be kept by the *Contractor*:
>
> (*a*) labour records
> (*b*) plant records
> (*c*) all invoices received from Subcontractors.

4.6.1.7 Procurement procedures

The *Project Manager* is obliged to disallow costs that were incurred because the *Contractor* did not follow an acceptance or procurement procedure stated in the Scope (clause 11.2(26) for Options C, D and E; clause 11.2(27) for Option F). The Scope should therefore state those procedures, where required.

> The acceptance or procurement procedures followed by the *Contractor* are as follows:
>
> (*a*) ....
> (*b*) ....

4.6.1.8 Bonds

Performance bond
If Option X13 has been chosen, the form of the performance bond should be incorporated into the Scope.

Ultimate holding company guarantee
If Option X4 has been chosen, the form of the ultimate holding company guarantee should be incorporated into the Scope.

Advanced payment bond
If Option X14 has been chosen and a bond is required, the form of the advanced payment bond should be incorporated into the Scope.

4.6.1.9 Subcontractors

It is necessary to state whether parts of the *works* may or may not be subcontracted. There is no nominated subcontracting in the NEC. If the *Client* requires a part of the *works* to be performed by a specific contractor, it is preferable to contract directly with that *Contractor*, where the *Client* can maintain control, and where the *Client* should not then be subject to compensation events as a result of enforcing a subcontractor's use. The *Client* will, however, take on the interface risk between the *Contractor* and the contractor directly employed by the *Client*. Where parts of the *works* may be subcontracted, the Scope should state what Subcontractors are acceptable to the *Client*.

> The *Contractor* may not subcontract the *works*
>
> **or**
>
> The following work may not be subcontracted:
>
> (*a*) ....
> (*b*) ....
>
> **or**
>
> The *Contractor* may subcontract part of the *works*
>
> **or**

The *Contractor* subcontracts the following work:

(*a*) ....

(*b*) ....

The following Subcontractors are acceptable to the *Client* for performing the work required by this contract:

(*a*) Kitchen Installations:
   1. Kitchen World Limited, 1 Cupboard Way, Croydon
   2. Mersea Limited, 1 Sea Road, Ipswich
(*b*) Furniture and Fittings.

The ECC has no nomination process as in traditional contracts.

The *Client* has two alternatives:

- direct appointment with other contractors or
- include a list of approved suppliers/contractors in the Scope.

4.6.1.10 Quality management

The *Contractor* is obliged to operate a quality management system that complies with the requirements stated in the Scope (clause 40.1). As part of this quality management system, the *Contractor* must provide a quality policy statement and a quality plan to the *Project Manager* for acceptance. The *Project Manager* will refer to the quality plan so that they can assess if the *Contractor* has failed to comply with their quality plan.

The *Contractor's* quality management system will include quality assurances such as

- samples of Plant and Materials and workmanship
- acceptance of Plant and Materials
- compliance with recognised good practice
- compliance with the manufacturer's recommendation
- ordering and supply of Plant and Materials
- handling, storing and fixing
- storage of Plant and Materials
- setting out the *works* (this is not covered within the contract conditions as it is with traditional contacts, so this must be stated in the Scope)
- statements of how the *Contractor* plans to do the work – detailed requirements
- instrumentation.

4.6.1.11 Security and protection

State details of the *Client's* security arrangements or requirements, and details for protecting existing services, structures and so on.

Provisions for ensuring the control of noise, cleanliness of access roads and so on should be covered.

4.6.1.12 Facilities and services to be provided by the *Contractor* for use by the *Client* and Others

According to clause 25.2, the *Client* and the *Contractor* provide services and other things as stated in the Scope. The Scope should therefore state the interfaces between contractors on the Site. Any services provided by one contractor to another or by or to the *Client* should also be stated, as well as responsibility for the provision and maintenance of facilities such as

- access roads, scaffolding, cranes and hoists, and water
- accommodation for the *Client's* and *Project Manager's* staff
- facilities and services for 'common use'
- fences, screens and hoardings
- temporary facilities.

> The following services are provided on Site by the *Client* during the periods stated: [storage, power supplies, water, compressed air, telephone]
>
> (*a*) ....
>
> (*b*) ....

4.6.1.13 Facilities and services to be provided by the *Contractor* for their own use

This includes everything not provided by the *Client*, such as

- offices and storage sheds
- welfare facilities and services
- measures for tidiness at work sites
- name board and advertising
- power and lighting
- water
- drainage
- communications
- temporary lighting
- temporary facilities and services coordination
- temporary roads, hardstandings and crossings
- fences, screens and hoarding.

It should be noted that this list is not exhaustive and that a list of this sort is not recommended for inclusion in the Scope. See below for a simple way to include all *Contractor*-provided facilities.

> The following services are provided by the *Contractor* during the periods stated:
>
> (*a*) ....
>
> (*b*) ....

4.6.1.14 Facilities and services to be provided by the *Client* for use by the *Contractor*

This is where the *Client* states the particulars of the facilities and services that will be provided by the *Client* at each site. This will cover items such as connection points or locations where water and electricity supplies can be utilised.

Free-issue items

Some *Clients* free-issue Plant and Materials to the *Contractor* in order to reduce the cost of the project, where the *Client* has agreements with suppliers that provide items to the *Client* at lower than trade prices. If this is the case, the Scope should be very clear about what it is that the *Client* is going to provide in order to avoid the situation where each Party thought the other Party was going to supply the item. Providing Plant and Materials may affect insurances. Another issue that needs to be considered is who is responsible for delivery/collection.

> This section describes what the *Client* is to supply specifically for the purpose of the *works*. The *Contractor* is to supply everything else required to Provide the Works.

4.6.1.15 Work provided

According to clause 31.2, the *Contractor* shows in each programme, among other things, the order and timing of the work of the *Client* and Others either as stated in the Scope or as last agreed, and any other information that the Scope requires the *Contractor* to show.

The Scope should therefore state what work the *Client* would do or Others not directly involved in this contract. Also included should be those things other than those stated in clause 31.2 that are required to be shown in each programme.

> The work of the *Client* and Others to be included in the programme are
>
> (*a*) ....
>
> (*b*) ....
>
> The *Contractor* shows on their programme submitted for acceptance
>
> (*a*) ....
>
> (*b*) ....

It should be noted that if the *Client* or Others do not work within the conditions stated in the Scope, the *Contractor* is entitled to a compensation event in accordance with clause 60.1(5).

4.6.1.16 Working with Others

This section details operations or other *works* within the Working Areas by Others under separate arrangements with the *Client*. A good way to deal with this is to list each operation or work by Others in this section, giving a brief description of each, and where, when and what they will be doing.

Co-operation clause 25.1

If the *Contractor* is required to co-operate with Others then the Scope should state what information they need to obtain and provide for them in connection with the *works*.

It is also important to ensure that it is clearly stated how the *Contractor* will share the Working Areas with Others.

Other responsibilities – clause 27.1

This clause states that the *Contractor* obtains approval of their design from Others where necessary. The clause therefore requires that the Scope is clear on whom the *Contractor* needs to obtain approval from for their design.

Sharing the Working Areas

According to clause 25.1, the *Contractor* shares the Working Areas with Others as stated in the Scope. The Working Areas are the Site and other areas defined by the *Contractor*, and Others are people such as other contractors and other people not directly connected with this contract. The Scope should therefore include a statement about who else would be working on the Site with whom the *Contractor* might come into contact.

> The *Contractor* shares the Working Areas with Others as follows:
>
> (*a*) [person/body] ....
>
> (*b*) [period of time] ....
>
> (*c*) [part of the Working Areas] ....

It may also be useful to show this information in the form of a restraints programme, which indicates the key milestone dates and other constraints such as works by other contractors.

4.6.1.17 Title to materials from excavation and demolition

The *Client* should state here the title to materials arising from excavations and demolitions.

According to clause 73.2, the *Contractor* has title to materials from excavation and demolition unless the Scope states otherwise. The Scope should therefore detail those materials from excavation and demolition to which the *Contractor* has no title.

> The *Contractor* has no title to materials from excavation and demolition
>
> **or**
>
> The *Contractor* has title to materials from excavation and demolition except as follows:
>
> (*a*) ....
>
> (*b*) ....

Consideration also needs to be given in the Scope to

- storage arrangements
- salvage of reclaimed materials
- credit to the *Client* for the sale of such materials.

> **Salvaged/reclaimed materials**
>
> The *Contractor* shall carefully take down and take to the *Client's* store the existing oak panelling in the old boardroom.
>
> The *Contractor* shall provide a method statement detailing how it proposes to dismantle the panelling, together with a sequence of operations for the reassembly of the panelling. This will include the identification and marking of the panelling, the measures taken to protect the panelling during the dismantling process and the method of protection for storage.
>
> Arrangements have been made for the panelling to be stored in the *Client's* stores at:
>
> Building 305
> Field Road
> Newbridge
> NW19 5UR
>
> Contact the Stores Manager on: 01488 555820 ext. 1234

4.6.1.18 Materials off Site

According to clause 42.1, the *Contractor* does not bring to the Working Areas those Plant and Materials that the Scope states are to be tested or inspected before delivery. The Scope should therefore state which Plant and Materials are to be tested or inspected before delivery to the Working Areas.

It should also be noted that there is no payment for Plant and Materials on the Site unless the *Client* has stated that they are willing to pay for them.

According to clause 71.1, the *Contractor* prepares for marking Equipment, Plant and Materials that are outside the Working Areas, as the Scope requires. The Scope should therefore state which items are to be prepared for marking, and how this is to be done.

> The *Contractor* prepares for marking Equipment, Plant and Materials that are outside the Working Areas as follows:
>
> (*a*) ....
>
> (*b*) ....

4.6.2 Work specifications

Work specifications should detail exactly what it is that the *Contractor* is to provide. It is therefore very important that the specifications are clear, concise and unambiguous about what it is the *Contractor* is to provide and price for.

It could include, for example, specifications for

- site clearance
- earthworks
- brickwork
- concrete
- reinforcement
- drawings.

For *Client*-designed work and performance, it will include specifications for *Contractor*-designed work.

Where Plant, Materials and workmanship specifications are dictated by the *Client*, these should be included in the Scope, as well as requirements for delivery and storage before their incorporation in the *works* and the provision of spares, operating manuals and the like.

4.6.2.1 Specific requirements for the methods, sequence and timing of the *works* and use of the Site

This section of the Scope will detail everything that will affect how, where, when and what will be done.

Great care needs to be taken when writing this section to ensure that it does not conflict, creating ambiguities or inconsistencies between this section and the remainder of the Scope.

This section will cover such information as

- design constraints on the methods, sequence and timing of the *works*
- the timing of the *works*
- restrictions on the use of the work site
- other restrictions and requirements
- working hours
- night working restrictions
- noise levels
- the *Client's* approval of publications
- the excavation of sand and gravel output (as specifications)
- explosives (as specifications).

4.6.2.2 Tests and inspections

The *Supervisor* is responsible for the quality of the *works* and for ensuring that the *works* comply with the Scope.

The *Supervisor* is responsible for testing and inspection of the *works* as the Scope requires. It is therefore extremely important that the Scope spells out clearly all tests and inspections, which must have been carried out before completion of an item, or section of the *works* will be given. The Scope should also state who provides the facilities and materials for the testing.

Clause 41.1 states that only those tests and inspections required by the Scope and the applicable law apply. It is therefore important to ensure that all the tests and inspections that are applicable to the *works* are stated in the Scope. Where any general specifications quote the detail tests required, and those are considered to be sufficient, there is no need to repeat them. It is necessary, however, to ensure that those tests comply with the requirements in the core clauses.

(*a*) Description of the test:
- objective, procedure and standards used in the test
- performed at what stage of the work
- method used
- materials, facilities and samples required to be provided by the *Contractor* and the *Client* for tests and inspections
- time required to perform the test
- person to conduct the test
- acceptable results and deviations
- any documents provided for and produced as a result of the test.

According to clause 41.2, the *Contractor* and the *Client* provide materials, facilities and samples for tests and inspections as stated in the Scope. Ensure that the tests stated in any general specifications include this information. If not, include it in the Scope, with reference to the relevant test and specification. For tests that are described in the Scope, refer to the list above for an indication of what should be detailed.

If Option X17 is chosen, the Scope should include details of tests to measure the performance of the *works* in operation for which low-performance damages are specified.

The following tests are done to measure the performance of the *works*:

(*a*) ....

(*b*) ....

4.6.3 Design

Clause 21.1 states that if the *Contractor* is required to design elements of the *works*, the Scope should state what parts of the *works* the *Contractor* is to design, and what the interfaces with the *Client* are.

For contracts with little *Contractor's* design, a list of what is left to be designed by the *Contractor* should be provided. For more comprehensive design-and-build contracts, a list of what has been designed by the *Client* should be given, with the *Contractor* being made responsible for designing the remainder.

***Contractor's* design**

The *Contractor* designs the following parts of the *works*:

(*a*) ....

(*b*) ....

or

The *Client* designs the following parts of the *works*; the *Contractor* designs everything else:

(*a*) ....

(*b*) ....

Also, state the interfaces with those parts of the *works* designed by the *Client*, and the design criteria. A design brief or performance specification for those parts of the *works* to be designed by the *Contractor* should be included in the Scope. The design brief for the parts of the *works* to be designed by the *Contractor* should cover the following and any other relevant matters:

- size or space limitations
- design standards and codes of practice (on what size paper and type of paper, how many copies to be made, to be retained by whom, etc.)
- plant, materials and workmanship specifications including references to relevant standards
- loading and capacity requirements
- operational performance requirements and design life.

According to clause 21.2, the *Contractor* submits the particulars of their design, as the Scope requires, to the *Project Manager* for acceptance. These elements of how and when particulars are submitted should be included in the Scope, including requirements for certification and/ or checking.

> **Example**
>
> The following are procedures that the *Contractor* is to follow in carrying out its design:
>
> (*a*) ....
>
> (*b*) ....

According to clause 22.1, the *Client* may use and copy the *Contractor's* design for any purpose connected with construction, use, alteration or demolition of the *works* unless otherwise stated in the Scope and for other purposes as stated in the Scope.

The Scope should therefore state any additional purposes for which the *Client* might wish to put the *Contractor's* design to use, for example using it to build the same thing again elsewhere.

> The *Client* may use and copy the *Contractor's* design for the following purposes:
>
> (*a*) ....
>
> (*b*) ....

It should also cover design sanctioning procedures, and cover details of the design particulars that the *Project Manager* wishes to see, together with the submission details and certification/acceptance procedure, and deal with *Contractor's* changes.

4.6.3.1 Design of Equipment

According to clause 23.1, the *Contractor* may be required to submit particulars of the design of an item of Equipment to the *Project Manager* for acceptance. If the *Client* requires the *Contractor* to design items of Equipment, the details of the Equipment and the design particulars should be detailed in the Scope in the same way as for the design of the *works*.

4.6.4 Health and safety requirements

Clause 27.4 requires health and safety requirements to be stated in the Scope. Since the *Contractor* has to adhere to the law (as does the *Client*), it is not necessary to reiterate parts of any statutes in the Scope. This clause therefore applies only to those requirements that are **additional** to those required by the law. The *Client* may have specific in-house requirements that require a greater level of health and safety than imposed by the law; for example, *Client*-specific requirements for airports, rail, petrochemical and power station sites. In this case, those requirements should be stated in the Scope or incorporated by reference, always ensuring that inconsistency between documents or between the law and the *Client's* requirements are eradicated.

A health and safety plan as required by the law (CDM Regulations) should be included.

4.6.5 Reinforcement schedules

These will appear as appendices to the Scope.

4.6.6 Drawings
4.6.6.1 Introduction

The designer needs to ask themselves some basic questions about the drawings.

Do the drawings give the *Contractor* sufficient information to Provide the Works? For example:

- Are all associated relevant drawings referred to?
- Are the appropriate parts of the Scope referred to?
- Is the terminology correct, such as *Project Manager* and *Supervisor*?
- Are there any 'woolly words', such as 'to the satisfaction of the *Project Manager*'?
- Are the drawings cross-referenced to any boundary limits given?

4.6.6.2 The importance of labelling

With any contract, care should be taken with labelling. If we look at the example in Figure 4.1, it shows a gas main, which runs between two points A and B. Unfortunately, the labelling indicates it as an existing and a 'new' 180 mm pipe. In this simple example, it is evident that the intent is for a new 180 mm polyethylene gas pipe between points A and B. However, the

Figure 4.1 A new gas main

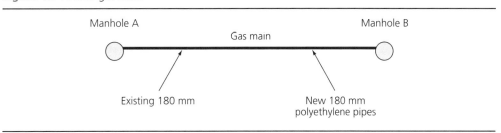

draughtsman's carelessness in labelling gives rise to an inconsistency under clause 17, and the *Project Manager* has to issue an instruction to clarify the Scope, which is a compensation event.

Even before the *Contractor* commences work on the Site they could have many compensation events, which will give rise to price and time changes if care is not taken in the documents.

4.7. Interface management

On multi-contract projects, one of the biggest challenges (or risks, depending on your perspective) is the management of the interface between the various contractors. Like most risks, this one is best avoided if at all possible, but the reality is that on most major projects with demanding programmes some interface between contractors is inevitable. The ECC makes it clear who carries the risk in the event of an error in the management of the interface between the *Contractor* and other contractors. Clause 60.1(5) makes it a compensation event, and therefore a *Client's* risk, if 'Others do not work within the times shown on the Accepted Programme, do not work within the conditions stated in the Scope or 'carry out work on the Site that is not stated in the Scope'.

The ECC Guidance Notes offer some good advice for situations where the interface between the *Contractor* and Others is complex. It emphasises the importance of planning and programming work (involving interfaces) as far as possible **before** the start of the contract. Other things to do before the start of the contract include the following:

- The start dates for work should be agreed, together with details of the work, its likely duration and facilities required to be provided by and for the *Contractor*.
- Details of the obligations of the Parties at each interface and the timing and programming arrangements should be agreed. This information may conveniently be provided in the form of interface schedules in the Scope to ensure that arrangements in the different contracts are 'back to back'.
- It should also be stated which party is to supply and maintain access (e.g. scaffolding or lifting equipment for plant), resources (e.g. for testing) and other services (e.g. power and water supply).
- On multi-contractor projects, several contractors may be sharing the same work site, or one contractor may be following another, in which case the first contractor might set up and leave the site set up on completion of their work. Difficulties nearly always occur with such interfaces. It should be clear in the Scope what is to be left at take over and how it is to be left.

It is important that not only the permanent works have a clear definition of when an item of work will be complete, but also any temporary, or temporary permanent works: for example, site accommodation, temporary lighting, electrics, ventilation, water supplies, access scaffolding and safety handrails.

It is important that you match what is left by one *Contractor* to what the next *Contractor* expects to find.

For instance, the Scope states:

Shaft A – 10.4 m diameter

On Completion of the *works* the *Contractor* shall leave an access scaffold in the shaft for use of the follow-on Contractor.

You may think this is simple enough, but consider the following scenario. This *Contractor* will leave an access scaffold, but what are the requirements? What standards must it meet? How will it be proved to the next *Contractor* that they can take it over?

We can see immediately that a lot more detail has to be put into this simple statement – even perhaps to the extent of a simple sketch or a list of criteria that the access scaffold must meet, for example

- minimum of two landings 1.2 × 2.4 m wide
- treads to be a minimum of 230 mm wide
- risers to be no more than 180 mm high, staircase to be a minimum of 1.2 m wide
- safety handrail on both sides to be 1.2 m high, enclosed with mesh
- 30 lux lighting at 2 m centres vertically on scaffold.

Also required is a signing-off procedure with the first *Contractor* to hand to the next to prove that the staircase is indeed fit for its purpose.

Another scenario is one where the *Contractor* gives notification that they have completed the shaft and the permanent works, and they request a Completion certificate from the *Project Manager*.

The response from the *Project Manager* is that the *Contractor* has not put in the access stairs yet, so the *Project Manager* will not give the *Contractor* a Completion certificate. The *Contractor* states that the access stairs are temporary works, but the *Project Manager* advises the *Contractor* that as far as their *works* are concerned, they are temporary/permanent works, which they must complete prior to a Completion certificate being issued.

If the *Project Manager* has not stipulated this requirement in the Scope, then an ambiguity/inconsistency exists that, when it is possible to apply the *contra proferentem* rule that the ambiguity/inconsistency is construed against the drafter, then the *Project Manager* could lose their argument. (*Contra proferentem* means that the interpretation of words works against the Party who drafted the words **or** who uses them as a basis for claim against another. For example, a plaintiff who sues for breach of a written contract can expect any ambiguity in the terms of the contract will be resolved against them.) If on the other hand it is clearly spelled out in the Scope, then the *Project Manager* will be correct to insist on it being completed prior to their issuing a Completion certificate.

A key consideration in all interface management is safety. The project team should think about the likely problem areas with regard to health, safety, security, facilities and so on.

The access to the curtilage of the Site is through a redundant petrol station. Specifically, the route into the Site is over redundant fuel tanks, which are covered by approximately 1 m of concrete.

On commencing the contract the *Contractor* notifies the *Project Manager* that they are proposing to bring onto the Site some heavy piling Equipment and other heavy Equipment, and wishes to have assurances that it is safe to bring the Equipment onto the Site.

Unfortunately, no site investigation work has been undertaken on these 20-year-old tanks, and the *Project Manager* faces the prospect of delays to the project, especially as the design team is unable to provide the assurances sought by the *Contractor*. As the *Project Manager* is unable to give assurances, they therefore instruct the *Contractor* to investigate and then fill the previously de-gassed and cleaned tanks with grade 40 concrete. (This would be a compensation event as a change to the Scope.)

The *Contractor* calls an early-warning meeting to notify the *Project Manager* that the reinforcement drawings for the new lift shaft call for 18 m-long 40 mm-diameter rebar to the waling beams. The new lift shaft is being constructed top down, and while these bars can be placed in the ground-level waling beams, the lower levels would require the bars to be lowered down vertically in a shaft that has personnel working below. This would be very dangerous, as it is very difficult to lower these heavy bars each weighing 200 kg safely. Therefore, the excavation work would have to stop while the rebar was lowered into the shaft. This stoppage in work had not been envisaged at the time of tender, and would delay the project.

The *Contractor* also pointed out that, once lowered, the rebar would be almost impossible to place in the waling beams.

The *Project Manager* agrees with the *Contractor* on both of these issues, and instructs the *Contractor* to cut the rebar to lengths that would enable easy placing in the walings and the safe lowering of the rebar, while work continued at the bottom of the shaft. (This would be a compensation event as a change to the Scope.)

4.8. General rules in drafting the Scope

The contract places great emphasis on clarity in terms of contract documentation. An essential element of documentation is to present the documents in a clear and structured way. So, careful consideration should be given at the outset to the structure and format of the contract documents.

4.8.1 Incorporating other documents into the Scope

Where the Scope is being drafted onto a blank sheet of paper, it is easier to incorporate the requirements of the ECC into the Scope while leaving the sense of the document intact. Where a specification or *Client's* requirements is incorporated into the Scope, problems could arise.

Where a standard specification or already-drafted specification is the basis of the Scope, there are two options available when drafting the Scope.

- Incorporate the specification into the Scope by reference, making sure that NEC terminology is adhered to, even if that is just by reading words in a different way. For example, a standard specification could be prefaced by an explanation of NEC terminology and could incorporate a table that includes items such as: 'Throughout this specification any reference to Engineer shall be deemed to mean *Project Manager*'. This has inherent difficulties, however. The ECC *Project Manager* does not have exactly the same duties as the traditional Engineer. Some of the duties of the Engineer are those of the ECC *Project Manager*, and some are those of the ECC *Supervisor*. By automatically reading one term for another, ambiguities may be introduced into the document unnecessarily.
- Incorporating the specification into the Scope by rewriting the specification into the format of the Scope, ensuring that all the requirements of the Scope are catered for – which is the preferred option. (The rewrite could take the form of reading the specification from start to finish and manually making the changes required.) This is clearly more time-consuming, but achieves a more cohesive and comprehensive Scope that should reduce the possibilities of disputes as a result of ambiguities and inconsistencies between documents. This proposed change also emphasises the importance of including sufficient time into the programme for the procurement of the project.

When compiling the Scope the drafter needs to consider if the information they are providing is

- essential
- relevant
- complete
- clear
- unambiguous.

4.8.2 General drafting rules

In general, a few rules apply that assist in maintaining the cohesiveness of the Scope.

- Avoid words promoting conflict/adversarialism, such as
  - reasonable
  - to someone's satisfaction
  - in the opinion of
  - suitable
  - appropriate
  - relevant.
- Avoid legal and commercial terms. The appropriate place for legal and commercial terms is in the Contract Data.
- Try to write a performance specification, particularly where the Scope is not totally defined.
- Documents are submitted for acceptance. The word 'approval' is not used in the NEC.
- Do not rely on past relationships. The NEC is different from other forms of contract; so do not rely on the fact that the *Contractor* knows the way your company works.
- Do not include any statements that refer to the tender. There should be no reference to the tender in any of the contract documents.

4.8.3 The classic statements

There are some classic 'woolly' statements with incorrect terminology that appear in many specifications. A list of some of these classic statements is given below:

- 'The *works* will be complete when in the **opinion of the Engineer** all work is complete.'
- 'The *Contractor* shall have been deemed to have allowed in their tender for **all tests that the Engineer may require.**'
- **'Work will be completed to the satisfaction of the Engineer.'**
- 'The *Contractor* shall allow for **all reasonable access** to the site.'
- 'The *Contractor* shall have been deemed to have visited the installation and to have **allowed for everything necessary to complete it.**'

If we look at the statements, we can see that they lack clarity and are woolly in the sense that they do not spell out clearly and concisely what it is the *Contractor* is to provide.

If they do not know what it is they are to provide how can they price for it? It also means that if a dispute occurs on an item there can be long arguments about what the clause actually means or was intended to mean rather than what it actually says.

Harry Haste, the *Project Manager*, is in a rush, his fees are tight and he sees no reason to reinvent the wheel. Consequently, he runs off copies of old specifications for the new contract. He is secure in the knowledge that his specification had always been very robust.

A typical example of his specification for the *works* follows.

Examination of typical traditional specification:

W1   Water mains
W1.1   If, in the opinion of the Engineer, there is undue delay in the application of the first hydraulic test, or of any subsequent tests, or if any length of main should fail the test, the Engineer may direct the Contractor to suspend main laying operations until the length or lengths of main have been satisfactorily tested.

[Note the woolly words 'in the opinion of' and 'satisfactorily', as well as the uncertainty regarding the Engineer's actions and the use of the term 'Engineer' – which should be *Client*.]

W1.2   After satisfactory completion of pressure testing, each valve on, and adjacent to, the pipeline shall be examined to witness that the opening/closing mechanisms function satisfactorily and are capable of functioning for their designated purpose. Isolating valves shall be examined by opening and closing the isolating gate three times. All tests and examinations shall be witnessed by the Engineer's staff and the Contractor shall provide a witnessed certificate to this effect to the Engineer.

[Note the woolly word 'satisfactorily' and the use of the wrong terminology. The witnessing of the tests should be by the *Supervisor*. If a preface had been included in this specification to the effect of 'read *Project Manager* for Engineer', then the *Project Manager* would have an obligation that is the *Supervisor's* under the *conditions of contract*, and a conflict would exist. Note also that the *Contractor* is required to provide notification of results under the *conditions of contract*, and this Scope paragraph requires an extra obligation of the *Contractor*.]

W2   Swabbing of water mains
W2.1   Swabs will be provided by the Purchaser. Temporary pipework shall be provided by the Contractor.

[Note the wrong terminology: Purchaser should be *Client*. Note also the vague nature of the statement. How many swabs will be provided? Where will/can they be obtained from?]

W3   Water supply for testing and swabbing
W3.1   For the purpose of the hydraulic testing of water-retaining structures and pipelines, the Purchaser will make available water from existing mains, at times and rates of flow to be decided by the Purchaser and agreed with the Engineer.

[Note the incorrect terminology: 'Purchaser' and 'Engineer' should be *Supervisor* in accordance with the Scope and *Contractor*, respectively. Note also that if the *Contractor* were to do the test, they are not involved in the decision of when the water is to be provided, although this could affect their programme.]

W3.2   Water will be provided free of charge to the Contractor for the first test. In the event of any part of the work having to be retested the Contractor shall be required to pay for the supply of water on a volume basis at the prevailing rate of the Purchaser.

[Note the incorrect terminology: 'Purchaser' should be *Client*.]

G1   Standards of materials
G1.1   15th Statement of the DoE Committee on Chemicals and Materials of Constructions for use in Public Water Supplies and Swimming Pools.
G1.2   The use of materials, including chemicals that do not meet the above criteria, shall be subject to the approval of the Engineer.

[Note that in the ECC, 'acceptance', not 'approval', is the terminology used. Also, 'Engineer' should be *Project Manager*.]

G2   Disinfection of pipework and structures
        Pipes, pumps and structures shall be disinfected in accordance with the following procedure:
        (a)   The Contractor shall provide, at least three weeks before carrying out the disinfection process, a Method Statement to the Engineer for its Approval.

[Note that in the ECC 'a statement of how the *Contractor* plans to do the work' is part of the *Contractor's* programme. The *Contractor* submits their programme to the *Project Manager* (not the Engineer) for acceptance (not approval). There are several programme revisions provided for in the *conditions of contract*, including where the *Project Manager* can ask for one at any time.]

        (b)   After satisfactory hydraulic testing, pipes, pumps, structures etc. shall be cleaned of all deleterious material.

[Note the use of vague words such as 'satisfactory'. The expected results of the test, as well as the details of how and when the test is to be carried out, should be provided.]

> *(c) The volume to be disinfected shall be filled with chlorinated water at a dose level of 20–25 mg/l free chlorine and left to stand for 24 hours. Large structures may have all surfaces thoroughly scrubbed down with heavily chlorinated water and the volume then filled with a lower dose level, 0.5 mg/l chlorinated water, and left for 24 hours.*
>
> *(d) The chlorinated water shall be drained away and disposed of in a <u>safe</u> and <u>satisfactory</u> manner. All <u>necessary</u> approvals for discharge shall be obtained by the Contractor. De-chlorination will be necessary to ensure that free chlorine discharged is below 0.1 mg/l, where discharge is to a watercourse, or drain leading to a watercourse.*

[Note the vague words 'safe', 'satisfactory' and 'necessary'. What is safe and satisfactory to the *Contractor* could be different from the *Project Manager's* view. Unless a published standard is quoted, the requirements should be stated in the Scope.]

> *(e) The volume shall then be refilled with potable water and left a further 24 hours.*
>
> *(f) <u>The Purchaser will take samples for bacteriological testing. The results of its test will take a minimum of three working days to provide a conclusive test.</u>*

[Note the incorrect terminology: 'Purchaser' should be *Client*. The Scope is required to state who provides samples, materials and facilities for testing. The criteria of the test should also be stated.]

> *(g) <u>If test results are unsatisfactory to the Purchaser, the above procedure shall be repeated until satisfactory results are achieved.</u>*

[Note the use of incorrect and vague terminology: 'Purchaser' and 'satisfactory'. The uncertainty of this statement could leave the *Contractor* having difficulties pricing accurately, or potentially adding conservative amounts of risk into their price.]

This emphasises the importance that the contract puts upon the Scope.

4.8.4 Conclusion

There can be a world of difference between what the **intent** of a clause is and what it actually states. Great care is required in the writing and drafting of specifications.

Many people do not realise the importance of the Scope and consequently more often than not the specifications remain very much like those found in the Joint Contracts Tribunal (JCT) or ICE contracts. Far too often old or similar documents are used with just a few words changed here and there. This is totally unsatisfactory. Little care or forethought is given to them and the seeds of dispute have inadvertently been set.

4.9. Site Information
4.9.1 Introduction

The Site Information is information that

- describes the Site and its surrounding
- is in the documents that the Contract Data states it is in.

Site information will cover items such as

- existing buildings on or adjacent to the Site
- existing mains services
- access for inspection of Site and buildings.

4.9.2 Using the Site Information

The Site Information has particular impact when the compensation event for physical conditions (clause 60.1(12)) is considered. In assessing the risk under the contract, the *Contractor* will take into account the Site Information (clause 60.2).

Those *Clients* who equate clause 60.1(12) with clause 12 of the ICE Conditions of Contract may choose to 'pass the risk' in clause 60.1(12) to the *Contractor*, as was so frequently done with ICE clause 12. It should be noted, however, that risks are not 'passed' but are reallocated. The *Client* is likely still to have to pay for that risk in one form or other, even if it is not as visible, for example, when the *Contractor* includes risk in their price, but that amount of risk cannot be separated from the rest of the price.

If a *Client* does choose to delete clause 60.1(12) from the *conditions of contract* using Option Z, then the Site Information (e.g. geological surveys) should not form part of the contract documents but should be made available as reference information about the Site and its surroundings. Only factual information should be made available, with the interpretation of the information being left to the *Contractor*. In addition, all references to Site Information should be removed from the documents, as should clauses 60.2 and 60.3 of the *conditions of contract*.

4.9.3 Impact of the Site Information for interfacing *Contractors*

Let us consider an example scenario.

The *Client* has carried out some enabling works; part of that is the site establishment of the work site known as Spring Field. The plan layout in the Site Information for the follow-on *Contractor* is as shown in Figure 4.2.

Figure 4.2 Site Information

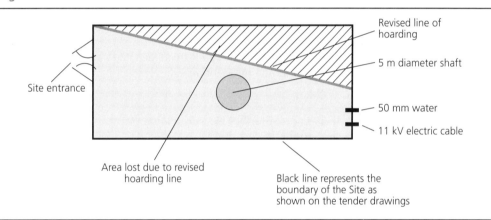

The drawing issued to the follow-on *Contractor* shows the working area to be as on drawing reference 100 Spring Field Dell Site Rev A.

The *Contractor* uses this Site Information in the preparation of their tender. When they arrive on the Site, they find that the area of the Site is somewhat different to that anticipated. The recourse they have is through compensation event 60.1(12), where the physical conditions affect the *Contractor*, taking into account the Site Information. The third bullet point of clause 60.1(12) requires the *Contractor* to have visited the Site and done what an experienced contractor would do. It is likely that the *Client* would rely on this in any defence against the compensation event. The *Contractor* should always ensure that they have visited the Site and done everything possible to ensure that they are familiar with the Site and its conditions.

This example indicates the great care required when dealing with interface information between *Contractors*.

With the advent of the CDM Regulations, many arguments can arise due to disagreement on how a Site has been left by the previous *Contractor* and how the following *Contractor* was advised they would find the Site.

4.9.4 Drawings issued for information purposes only

If an *Client* issues drawings 'for information purposes only' (Figure 4.3), what is the real status of that drawing? What if that information conflicts with other information provided?

Figure 4.3 For information purposes only

In accordance with clause 60.2, the *Client* takes the responsibility for information provided in the Site Information. The *Client* cannot shrug off that responsibility by saying that the drawing was provided 'for information purposes only'. It remains their responsibility, and they are liable under the contract if that information is incorrect or conflicting.

If the information is conflicting, then the *contra proferentem* rule (included in clause 60.3) applies, and the information is interpreted in favour of the *Contractor* (since it was the *Client* who drafted it).

This emphasises that the information provided in the Site Information is extremely important and cannot just be thrown together in a haphazard fashion. The *Client* should ensure that it makes sense and that it represents accurately the Site, because the *Contractor* relies on this information in putting together their tender.

4.9.5 The Site, *boundaries of the site* and Working Areas

It is important to understand the terminology used in the contract. This section looks at the difference between the terms

■ the Site
■ *boundaries of the site*
■ Working Areas.

4.9.5.1 The Site

The Site is defined as the area within the *boundaries of the site* stated in the Contract Data. This area comprises locations provided by the *Client* for the *works*. The definition of the Site is important, as it relates to

■ *access dates*
■ compensations events (e.g. the *Client* fails to give access to the Site by the date shown on the Accepted Programme)
■ title to objects/items within the Site
■ definition of the *Client's* risks (i.e. 'use or occupation of the Site')
■ termination – the *Client* may instruct the *Contractor* to leave the Site.

4.9.5.2 The *boundaries of the site*

The Site is defined as the area within the *boundaries of the site* (stated in the Contract Data). This area comprises locations provided by the *Client* for the *works*. It is usually identified in Contract Data part one by the *Client* by naming a drawing on which the Site can be identified, and perhaps outlining in highlighter the *boundaries of the site* (Figure 4.4).

4.9.5.3 The Working Areas

The concept of Working Areas is introduced in recognition of the fact that the *Contractor* often makes use of other areas to provide the *works*. Such areas may include batching plant, laydown

Figure 4.4 The Site, *boundaries of the site* and Working Areas

areas, temporary workshops and the like. For example, in Figure 4.4 the *Client* has stated the location of the site and its *boundaries*.

The *Contractor*, when completing part two of the Contract Data, might decide that the area of the Site is insufficient to enable them to prefabricate piling reinforcement cages for the new building, and they also plan to set up a temporary bar reinforcement bending workshop. By chance there is a vacant site across the road and adjacent to the site that will be suitable for their requirements.

The *Contractor* starts negotiations with the landowner – which they know they will not have concluded prior to them submitting their tender. They therefore insert in Contract Data part two not the specific site name but a more generic one that simply states 'laydown and prefabrication facilities'.

Alternatively, it could transpire that, during the hurly-burly of preparing their tender for submission, the *Contractor* forgets to put into the tender the other *working areas* that they require in order to Provide the Works. They only discover this omission after the contract has been let. In this case, the *Contractor* should write to the *Project Manager* under clause 16.3, submitting a proposal for adding to the Working Areas and stating their reasons why they require the additional area. As long as the proposal is necessary for providing the *works* and it will be used for work, which is in the contract, the *Project Manager* should have no objection.

The Working Areas have significance in that under clause 70.2 the title that the *Contractor* has in Plant and Materials brought within the Working Areas passes to the *Client*. Title to Plant and Materials passes back to the *Contractor* if it is removed from the Working Areas with the *Project Manager's* permission. Working Areas is discussed in greater detail in Chapter 2 of Book Four, which deals with the Schedule of Cost Components, since the Working Areas' identification impacts on Defined Cost.

Procuring an Engineering and Construction Contract
ISBN 978-0-7277-6184-2

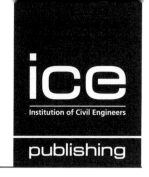

Appendix 4
Scope clauses

A4.1. Scope clauses   The following are clauses that appear in the *conditions of contract* and that require further information to be inserted into the Scope.

11.2(2)	Completion is when the *Contractor* has ■ done all the work which the Scope states is to be done by the Completion Date and ■ corrected notified Defects which would have prevented the *Client* from using the *works* and Others from doing their work. If the work which the *Contractor* is to do by the Completion Date is not stated in the Scope, Completion is when the *Contractor* has done all the work necessary for the *Client* to use the *works* and for Others to do their work.
11.2(6)	A Defect is ■ a part of the *works* which is not in accordance with the Scope or ■ a part of the *works* designed by the *Contractor* which is not in accordance with the applicable law or the *Contractor's* design which the *Project Manager* has accepted.
11.2(9)	Equipment is items provided and used by the *Contractor* to Provide the Works and which the Scope does not require it to include in the *works*.
11.2(15)	To Provide the Works means to do the work necessary to complete the *works* in accordance with the contract and all incidental work, services and actions which the contract requires.
11.2(16)	Scope is information which ■ specifies and describes the *works* or ■ states any constraints on how the *Contractor* Provides the Works and is either ■ in the documents which the Contract Data states it is in or ■ in an instruction given in accordance with this contract.
13.2	If the Scope specifies the use of a communication system, a communication has effect when it is communicated through the communication system specified in the Scope. If the Scope does not specify a communication system, a communication has effect when it is received at the last address notified by the recipient for receiving communications or, if none is notified, at the address of the recipient stated in the Contract Data.
17.2	The *Project Manager* or the *Contractor* notifies the other as soon as either becomes aware that the Scope includes an illegal or impossible requirement. If the Scope does include an illegal or impossible requirement, the *Project Manager* gives an instruction to change the Scope appropriately.
20.1	The *Contractor* Provides the Works in accordance with the Scope.
21.1	The *Contractor* designs the parts of the *works* which the Scope states the *Contractor* is to design.
21.2	The *Contractor* submits the particulars of its design as the Scope requires to the *Project Manager* for acceptance. A reason for not accepting the *Contractor's* design is that it does not comply with either the Scope or the applicable law. The *Contractor* does not proceed with the relevant work until the *Project Manager* has accepted its design.

22.1	The *Client* may use and copy the *Contractor's* design for any purpose connected with construction, use, alteration or demolition of the *works* unless otherwise stated in the Scope and for other purposes as stated in the contract. The *Contractor* obtains from a Subcontractor equivalent rights for the *Client* to use material prepared by the Subcontractor.
25.1	The *Contractor* co-operates with Others, including in obtaining and providing information which they need in connection with the *works*. The *Contractor* shares the Working Areas with Others as stated in the Scope.
25.2	The *Client* and the *Contractor* provide services and other things as stated in the Scope. Any cost incurred by the *Client* as a result of the *Contractor* not providing the services and other things which it is to provide is assessed by the *Project Manager* and paid by the *Contractor*.
27.4	The *Contractor* acts in accordance with the health and safety requirements stated in the Scope.
31.2	The *Contractor* shows on each programme submitted for acceptance ■ … ■ the order and timing of work of the *Client* and Others as last agreed with them by the *Contractor* or, if it not so agreed, as stated in the Scope, ■ … ■ other information which the Scope requires the *Contractor* to show on a programme submitted for acceptance. A programme issued for acceptance is in the form stated in the Scope.
31.3	Within two weeks of the *Contractor* submitting a programme for acceptance, the *Project Manager* notifies the *Contractor* of the acceptance of the programme or the reasons for not accepting it. A reason for not accepting a programme is that ■ the *Contractor's* plans which it shows are not practicable ■ it does not show the information which this contract requires ■ it does not represent the *Contractor's* plans realistically or ■ it does not comply with the Scope. If the *Project Manager* does not notify acceptance or non-acceptance within the time allowed, the *Contractor* may notify the *Project Manager* of that failure. If the failure continues for a further 1 week after the *Contractor's* notification, it is treated as acceptance by the *Project Manager* of the programme.
35.2	The *Client* may use any part of the *works* before Completion has been certified. The *Client* takes over the part of the *works* when it begins to use it, except if the use is ■ for a reason stated in the Scope or ■ to suit the *Contractor's* method of working.
40.1	The *Contractor* operates a quality management system which complies with the requirements stated in the Scope.
41.1	This clause only applies to tests and inspections required by the Scope or the applicable law.
41.2	The *Contractor* and the *Client* provide materials, facilities and samples for tests and inspections as stated in the Scope.
42.1	The *Contractor* does not bring to the Working Areas those Plant and Materials which the Scope states are to be tested or inspected before delivery until the *Supervisor* has notified the *Contractor* that they have passed the test or inspection.
43.1	Until the *defects date*, the *Supervisor* may instruct the *Contractor* to search for a Defect. The *Supervisor* gives reasons for the search with the instruction. Searching may include ■ uncovering, dismantling, re-covering and re-erecting work ■ providing facilities, materials and samples for tests and inspections done by the *Supervisor* and ■ doing tests and inspections which the Scope does not require.

50.2	The *Contractor* submits an application for payment to the *Project Manager* before each assessment date setting out the amount the *Contractor* considers is due at the assessment date. The *Contractor's* application for payment includes details of how the amount has been assessed and is in the form stated in the Scope.
60.1(5)	The *Client* or Others ■ do not work within the times shown on the Accepted Programme ■ do not work within the conditions stated in the Scope or ■ carry out work on the Site that is not stated in the Scope.
60.1(16)	The *Client* does not provide materials, facilities and samples for tests and inspections as stated in the Scope.
71.1	The *Supervisor* marks Equipment, Plant and Materials which are outside the Working Areas if ■ this contract identifies them for payment and ■ the *Contractor* has prepared them for marking as the Scope requires.
73.2	The *Contractor* has title to materials from excavation and demolition unless the Scope states otherwise.
A55.1	Information in the Activity Schedule is not Scope or Site Information. If the activities on the Activity Schedule do not relate to the Scope, the *Contractor* corrects the Activity Schedule.
C55.1	Information in the Activity Schedule is not Scope or Site Information.
B, D56.1	Information in the Bill of Quantities is not Scope or Site Information.
C, D, E11.2(26) and F11.2(27)	Disallowed Cost is cost which the *Project Manager* decides ■ ... ■ was incurred only because the *Contractor* did not ■ follow an acceptance or procurement procedure stated in the Scope 　– ... (clause F11.2(27) does not include this next part of Disallowed Cost) and the cost of ... ■ correcting Defects caused by the *Contractor* not complying with a constraint on how it is to Provide the Works stated in the Scope ■ ...
C, D, E52.2 and F52.3	The *Contractor* keeps these records ■ ... ■ other records as stated in the Scope.
X4.1	If the *Contractor* is a subsidiary of another company, the *Contractor* gives to the *Client* a guarantee of the *Contractor's* performance from the ultimate holding company of the *Contractor* in the form set out in the Scope. If the guarantee was not given by the Contract Date, it is given to the *Client* within four weeks of the Contract Date.
X8.4	The *undertakings to Others*, *Subcontractor undertaking to Others* and *Subcontractor undertaking to the Client* are in the form set out in the Scope.
X9.1	The *Client* owns the *Contractor's* rights over material prepared for the design of the *works* except as stated otherwise in the Scope. The *Contractor* obtains other rights for the *Client* as stated in the Scope and obtains from a Subcontractor equivalent rights for the *Client* over the material prepared by the Subcontractor. The *Contractor* provides to the *Client* the documents which transfer these rights to the *Client*.

X10.1(4)	The Information Model Requirements are the requirements identified in the Scope for creating the Information Model.
X13.1	The *Contractor* gives the *Client* a performance bond, provided by a bank or insurer which the *Project Manager* has accepted, for the amount stated in the Contract Data and in the form set out in the Scope. A reason for not accepting the bank or insurer is that its commercial position is not strong enough to carry the bond. If the bond was not given by the Contract Date, it is given to the *Client* within four weeks of the Contract Date.
X14.2	The advanced payment bond is issued by a bank or insurer which the *Project Manager* has accepted. A reason for not accepting the proposed bank or insurer is that its commercial position is not strong enough to carry the bond. The bond is for the amount of the advanced payment which the *Contractor* has not repaid and is in the form set out in the Scope. Delay in making the advanced payment is a compensation event.
X15.3	The *Contractor* may use the material provided by it under the contract for other work unless ■ the ownership of the material has been given to the *Client* or ■ it is stated otherwise in the Scope.
X15.4	The *Contractor* retains copies of drawings, specifications, reports and other documents which record the *Contractor's* design for the *period for retention*. The copies are retained in the form stated in the Scope.
X16.3	If stated in the Contract Data or agreed by the *Client*, the *Contractor* may give the *Client* a retention bond, provided by a bank or insurer which the *Project Manager* has accepted, for the total amount to be retained and in the form set out in the Scope. A reason for not accepting the bank or insurer is that its commercial position is not strong enough to carry the bond. Any amount retained after the *Contractor* gives the *Client* a retention bond is paid to the *Contractor* in the next assessment.
X22.1(3)	Stage One and Stage Two have the meanings given to them in the Scope.
X22.2(2)	Within one week of the *Contractor* submitting a forecast for acceptance, the *Project Manager* either accepts the forecast or notifies the *Contractor* of the reasons for not accepting it. A reason for not accepting the forecast is that ■ it does not comply with the Scope or ■ it includes work which is not necessary for Stage One.
X22.3(1)	The *Contractor* submits its design proposals for Stage Two to the *Project Manager* for acceptance in accordance with the submission procedure stated in the Scope.
X22.3(3)	If the submission is not accepted, the *Project Manager* gives reasons. A reason for not accepting a *Contractor's* submission is that ■ it does not comply with the Scope ■ it will cause the *Client* to incur unnecessary costs to Others or ■ the *Project Manager* is not satisfied that the Prices or any changes to the Prices have been properly assessed.
X22.4(2)	The *Contractor* obtains approvals and consents from Others as stated in the Scope.
X22.6(1)	(1) The *Project Manager* issues a notice to proceed to Stage Two when ■ the *Contractor* has obtained approvals and consents from Others as stated in the Scope ■ …
X22.6(3)	(3) If the *Project Manager* does not issue a notice to proceed to Stage Two because ■ the *Project Manager* and the *Contractor* have not agreed the total of the Prices for Stage Two or ■ the *Contractor* has failed to achieve the performance requirements stated in the Scope the *Client* may appoint another contractor to complete the Stage Two *works*.
Y1.6	The *Contractor* submits proposals for adding a Supplier to the Named Suppliers to the *Project Manager* for acceptance. A reason for not accepting is that the addition of the Supplier does not comply with the Scope. The *Client,* the *Contractor* and the Supplier sign the Joining Deed after acceptance.

Procuring an Engineering and Construction Contract
ISBN 978-0-7277-6184-2

ICE Publishing: All rights reserved
http://dx.doi.org/10.1680/pecc.61842.151

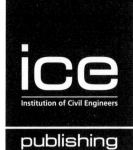

Index